Class Notes Statistics 1100

To accompany: Mind on Statistics, 5ed
University of Connecticut

Adelstein | McLaughlin

CENGAGE
Learning·

Australia • Brazil • Japan • Korea • Mexico • Singapore • Spain • United Kingdom • United States

CENGAGE
Learning·

Class Notes Statistics 1100: To accompany:
Mind on Statistics, 5ed, University of
Connecticut

Alexandra Adelstein
Kathleen McLaughlin

Custom Project Manager:

Marta Healey-Gerth

Manufacturing & Inventory Coordinator:

Kristina VanBuskirk

Premedia Content Project Manager:

Chris Doughman

Intellectual Property Project Manager:

Brian Methe

Cover Images:

Getty Images*

For product information and technology assistance, contact us at
Cengage Learning Customer & Sales Support, 1-800-354-9706

For permission to use material from this text or product,
submit all requests online at **cengage.com/permissions**
Further permissions questions can be emailed to
permissionrequest@cengage.com

Compilation © 2015 Cengage Learning

ISBN: 978-1-305-75997-8

WCN: 01-100-101

Cengage Learning
20 Channel Center Street
Boston, MA 02210
USA

Cengage Learning is a leading provider of customized learning solutions with
office locations around the globe, including Singapore, the United Kingdom,
Australia, Mexico, Brazil, and Japan. Locate your local office at:

www.international.cengage.com/region.

Cengage Learning products are represented in Canada by Nelson Education, Ltd.

For your lifelong learning solutions, visit **www.cengage.com/custom.**

Visit our corporate website at **www.cengage.com.**

Class Notes: Statistics 1100

To accompany:
Mind on Statistics, 5ed
Utts|Heckard

University of Connecticut
Department of Statistics
Prepared by
Alexandra Adelstein
and
Kathleen McLaughlin

CLASS NOTES
Statistics 1100

University of Connecticut

Department of Statistics

Contents

One Sample Inference

Statistics - An Overview

Variation is everywhere. Individuals vary; repeated measurements on the same individual vary; almost everything varies over time. Because variation is everywhere, conclusions are uncertain. Statistics gives us a language and rules for talking about uncertainty. Our task this semester will be to become acquainted with the terminology and mathematics of statistical methodology.

We can't escape variation and uncertainty. Learning about statistics enables us to live more comfortably with these realities.

Chapter 1

Statistics Success Stories and Cautionary Tales

1. Importance of understanding data, organizing data, displaying the data effectively

2. Baseline rates along w/ percent changes

3. Observational studies vs. randomized experiments

Statistics: Statistics is a collection of procedures and principles for gathering data and analyzing information to help people make decisions when faced with uncertainty.

How many pills do seniors (+65 years) typically take daily?

ideally non-overlapping and same width

Table

Categories	Relative frequencies
1 - 3	23 %
4 - 9	46 %
10 - 19	25 %
20 or more	6 %
	$\sum = 100\%$

Note: 20% of insured seniors said that they took no medication daily

Categories	Relative frequencies
0	→ 20 %
1 - 3	→ 80% of 23% = .8(23%) = 18.4 %
4 - 9	→ 80% of 46% = 2ND enter on calc = 38.6%
10 - 19	" 20 %
20 or more	" 4.8 %

80% {

$\sum \approx 100\%$

2

Obesity Rates in United States

→ percents

50 states in percent form

- 2006

28.7 24.9 20.8 26.4 22.7 16.9 19.6 22.9
21.5 21.9 25.5 18.1 22.4 23.9 26.2 24.3
23.2 26.7 27.5 22.0 23.4 18.6 25.6 23.1
29.5 25.1 19.9 24.4 21.2 21.6 21.4 21.1

21.7 24.7 24.6 24.8 25.4 22.2 24.5 19.5
26.2 24.1 26.5 25.8 20.8 19.5 23.3 22.4
28.6 22.7 21.7

- 2009

31.0 24.8 25.5 30.5 24.8 18.6 20.6 27.0
19.7 25.2 27.2 22.3 24.5 26.5 29.5 27.9
28.1 31.5 33.0 25.8 26.2 21.4 29.6 24.6
34.4 30.0 23.2 27.2 25.8 25.7 23.3 25.1
24.2 29.3 27.9 28.8 31.4 23.0 27.4 24.6
29.4 29.6 32.3 28.7 23.5 22.8 25.0 26.4
31.1 28.7 24.6

Obesity Rates in United States

Dot plot

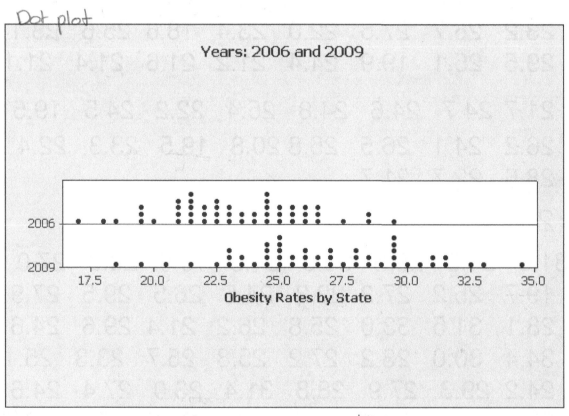

Years: 2006 and 2009

Obesity Rates by State

Overall, obesity rates ↑ b/c shifted to right

Case Study 1.2: Safety in the Skies?

starting points

Without knowing the baseline rates, a % increase or decrease may appear to be more significant than it actually is

Air traffic control errors

1997: 746 errors

1998: 878 errors

Calculate % increase

$$\frac{(\text{new number} - \text{old number})}{\text{old number}} \times 100$$

Baseline rate

1997: 4.8 errors per 1 million flights

1998: 5.5 errors/1 mil flights

cross multiply

$$\frac{4.8 \text{ errors}}{1 \text{ mil flights}} = \frac{746 \text{ errors}}{x \text{ mil flights}}$$

$$4.8x = 746$$

$$x \approx 155 \text{ mil flights}$$

$$\frac{5.5 \text{ errors}}{1 \text{ mil flights}} = \frac{878 \text{ errors}}{x \text{ mil flights}}$$

$$5.5x = 878$$

$$x \approx 160 \text{ mil flights}$$

$$\frac{(878 - 746)}{746} \times 100 \approx 20\%$$

20% can seem large, but when baseline rates are taken into account it's not that large

Delve a little more and see that flight safety hasn't rlly become more dangerous b/c rather insignificant

5

Case Study 1.5: Does Prayer Lower Blood Pressure?

Study: Sample of 2391 adults age 65 and older

Followed the individuals for 6 years

2 measurement variables/quantitative variables
- time spent praying weekly
- average blood pressure weekly

This is an observational study
- collecting info on participants, but they are not asked to do anything differently

Conclusion: those who regularly prayed were 40% less likely to have high blood pressure

Note: We don't know the baseline rate of high blood pressure in the older population

Valid to say: 2 variables are related

Invalid to say: praying <u>caused</u> the reduction in high blood pressure

In observational studies, we cannot <u>prove</u> cause + effect

Maybe some other variable that we didn't measure is causing the reduction in high blood pressure

Hartford Courant Article: 1/26/2009

- Infant deaths blamed on accidental strangulation in bed quadrupled between 1984 and 2004.

- The trend coincided with a sharp increase in bed-sharing of babies and parents.

Baseline rates:
1984: 2.8 deaths /100,000 babies
2004: 12.5 deaths/100,000 babies

Hartford Courant Article: 1/26/2009

2 variables: categorical (qualitative) variables

1. Bed-sharing   2. Deaths due to strangulation

     / \   / \

   yes   no   yes   no

Observational study: cannot prove cause + effect

     Clearly there is a logical connection

Calculate % increase: $\dfrac{(\text{new \#} - \text{old \#})}{\text{old \#}} \times 100$

$$\frac{\left(\frac{12.5}{100,000} - \frac{2.8}{100,000}\right)}{\frac{2.8}{100,000}} \times 100 \approx 346\% \text{ increase}$$

Article said: "rate quadrupled from 1984 to 2004"

     2004 rate = 1984 rate + increase

                 ↓

           $x + 346\% (1984 \text{ rate})$

          ↓

            $x + 3.5x$

            $4.5x$

             ↑

     where "quadrupled" comes from

        $4.5x \approx 4$ times 1984 rate

8

Case Study 1.6: Does Aspirin Reduce Heart Attack Rates?

Controlled randomized experiment

	Heart attacks	# of participants
Aspirin	104	11,037
Placebo	189	11,034

> randomly assigned!

Is the difference significant enough to recommend an aspirin a day?

more decimal

Aspirin $\frac{104}{11037} = .\frac{0094}{1} = \boxed{\frac{9.4}{1000.}}$ ← About 9 heart attacks per 1000 participants who took daily aspirin

Placebo $\frac{189}{1034} = .\frac{0171}{1} = \frac{17.1}{1000}$

In aspirin group, heart attack rate was about half the rate in the placebo group

Since this is a controlled randomized experiment, we can conclude that the aspirin <u>caused</u> the reduction

Chapter 2: Turning Data into Information

- What kinds of data should we collect? *Quantitative   Qualitative*

  How? Randomized experiment or observational study?

- How can we graphically display our data? *tell the story about the data*

- How can we numerically summarize our data?
  *mean
  median
  st deviation
  percentiles*

- How can we make generalizations based on our data?
  Use "sample data" to generalize to our population

Variable: A characteristic that can differ from one observational unit to the next.

1. Do you smoke? *yes or no*
   categorical / Qual

2. How do you rank UConn among the colleges to which you applied?
   Qual (ordinal)

3. What is your GPA?
   Quan, continuous

4. How many brothers and sisters do you have? *Quan, discrete*

Types of variables

Qualitative (categorical)
A subset of qual is ordinal (ranked data)

Quantitative numerical
discrete → count data
continuous → measurement data

Variable: A characteristic that can differ from one observational unit to the next.

5. What is your pulse rate?

Quan, continuous

6. Have you ever donated blood?

Qual

7. How much did you spend on books and supplies this semester?

Quan, continuous

↑

$ is usually cont

Questions about the relationship between two variables. bivariate data

x = Avg cholestrol level vs. y = heart attack
 Quan, cont   categorical
                  y / \ n

- ## Explanatory Variable:

  independent

  x-axis

  } often 2 variables follow this format

- ## Response Variable:

  dependent

  y-axis

  Y ↑
  → x

Ex: ① GPA @ UConn → Quan continuous

  ② Acceptance into school of ed → categorical

Sometimes 2 variables are simply related but not necessarily explanatory/response

Ex: SAT scores < math / reading   Are they related?

Population Data   vs.   Sample Data

fixed values

But they are difficult
    to calculate
(time consuming, costly)

Statistics can be
calculated, but they
vary from sample to
    sample

Parameters   vs.   Statistics

numerical
Characteristics of
a population

numerical
Characteristics
of a sample

Population

All Ucon
Students

Sample of
Students

↑
do all calculations

Parameters:
  % of students who smoke
  Avg # of credits taken per semester

Statistics
  % who smoke
  Avg # credits

17

Summarizing Categorical Variables

Qualitative

1. <u>C</u>ount how many observations fall into each category.

   Counts = frequencies

2. Calculate the percentage in each category.

   or decimal or fraction

   relative frequency

Table 2.1 Seatbelt Use by Twelfth-Graders When Driving

Response *(Categories)*	Count *(Frequency)*	Percent *(Relative Frequency)*
Always	1686	55.4%
Most times	578	19.0%
Sometimes	414	13.6%
Rarely	249	8.2%
Never	115	3.8%
Total	3042	100%

©2006 Thomson Higher Education

Note: Groups must be well defined.

→ "Most times" would need definition → ≈ 75%

$\Sigma = 3042$
↑
Sum (capital sigma)

$\dfrac{115}{3042} \times 100$

19

Visual Summaries for Categorical Variables

1.   Pie Charts:

interchangeable

2.   Bar Graphs:

3.   Clustered Bar Graphs:

allows for 2 categorical
variables on x-axis

Pie Chart

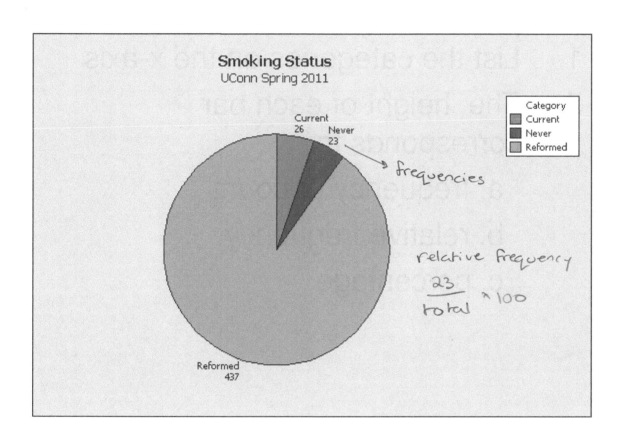

Bar Graphs

1. List the categories on the x-axis
2. The height of each bar corresponds to:
   a. frequency or count
   b. relative frequency
   c. percentage

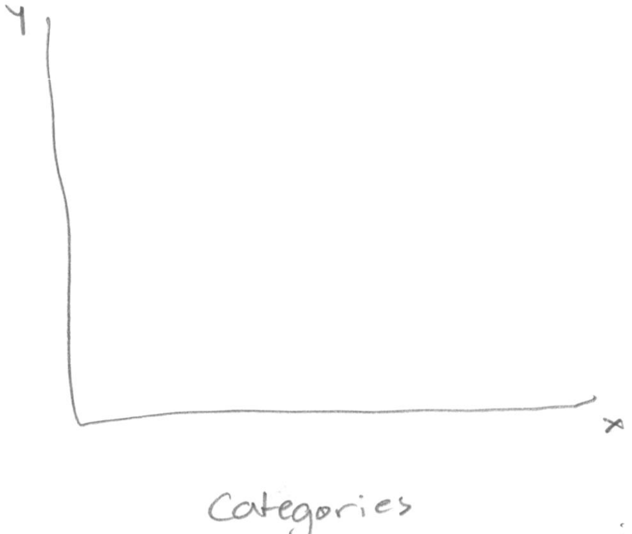

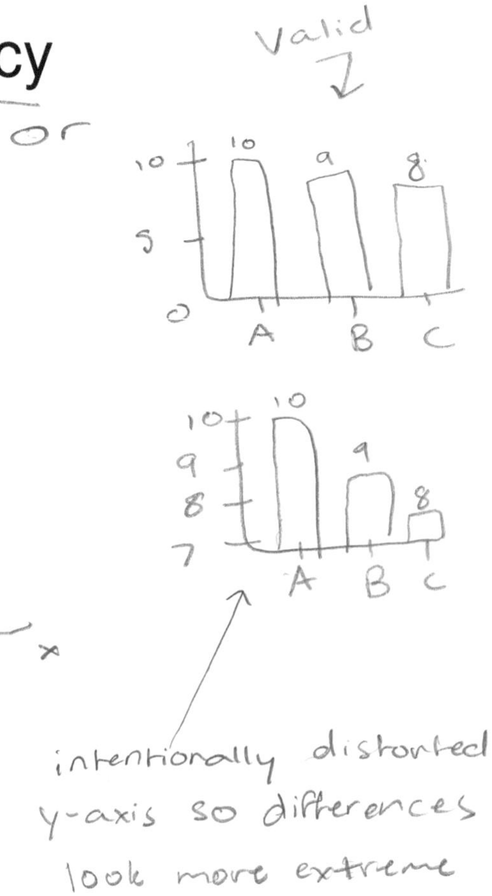

Valid

Categories

intentionally distorted y-axis so differences look more extreme

Bar Chart using Counts

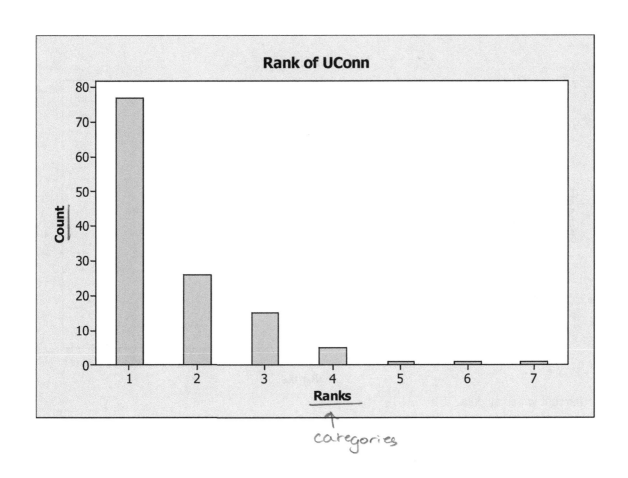

Bar Chart Using Percents

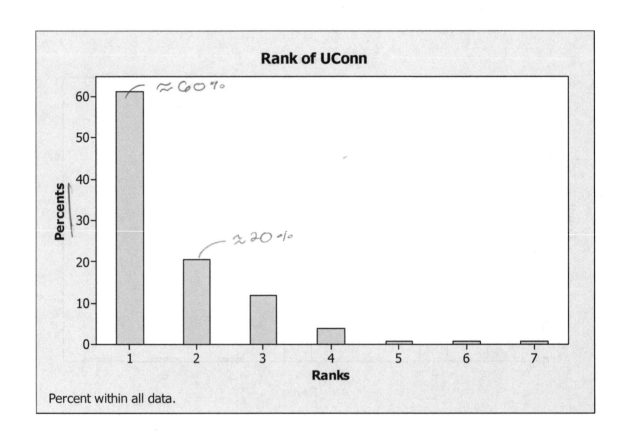

Bar Chart Using Graphing Calculator

- Results of randomly picking a number from 0 to 10

Clustered Bar Graph

1. Lighting conditions (outer variable)

2. Myopia level (inner variable)

3. Relative frequencies

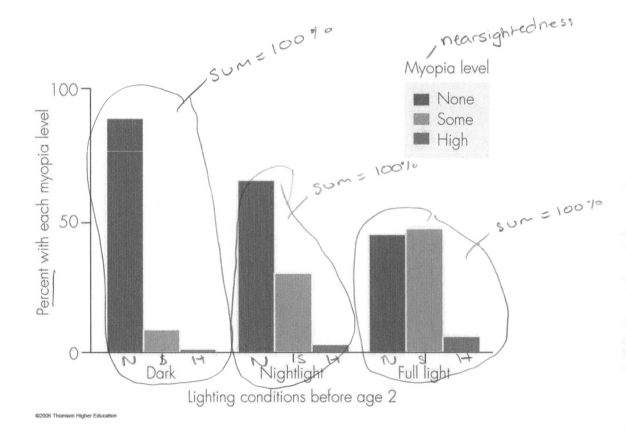

Clustered Bar Chart

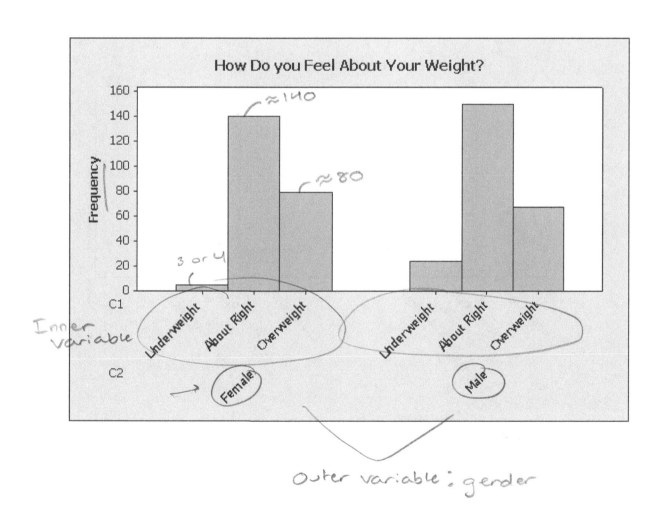

Clustered Bar Chart

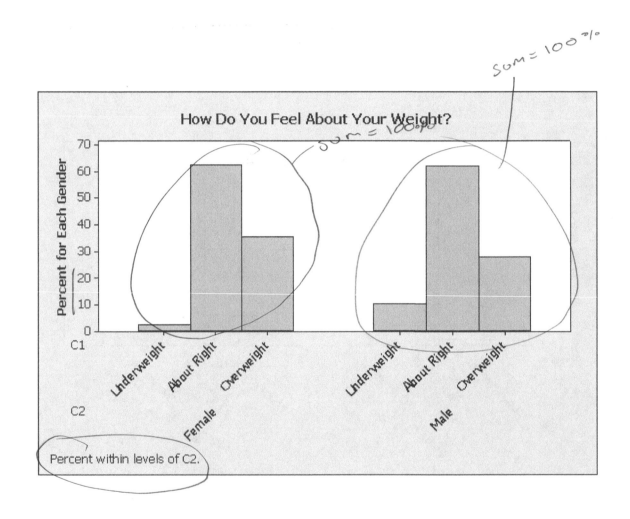

How Do You Feel About Your Weight?

Sum = 100%

Sum = 100%

Percent within levels of C2.

numerical data
we can perform math calculations

Summarizing Quantitative Data

→ how the data behaves

- The **distribution** of a quantitative variable is the overall pattern of how often possible values occur.

1. Location: *→ where does the data lie numerically? where is the center?*

2. Spread: *→ what is the variation in the data?*

3. Shape: *→ typical shape:*
   ① normal
   ② uniform
   ③ skewed / to right positively skewed
   ④ skewed to left / negatively skewed

4. Outliers
   unusual data points

29

An outlier is a data point that is "not consistent" with the "bulk" of the data.

unusual data value

to find these → graph the data

If you find outliers →
    is the outlier valid?
            or
        is it an error?

Visual Summaries for Quantitative Variables

1. Histograms:

    Minitab: All 4 graphs
    TI-84: #1 and #4

2. Dotplots:

3. Stem-and-leaf plots: easy to create by hand
    for small datasets
    Uses the digits in dataset
    to make the graph

    ```
    4 | 6 7 7
    5 | 4 5
    6 | 1
    ```

4. Boxplots:

    outliers

Table 2.5 The First Ladies of the United States of America

Name	Born—Died	Age at Death
Martha Dandridge Custis Washington	1731—1802	71
Abigail Smith Adams	1744—1818	74
Martha Wayles Skelton Jefferson	1748—1782	34
Dolley Payne Todd Madison	1768—1849	81
Elizabeth Kortright Monroe	1768—1830	62
Louisa Catherine Johnson Adams	1775—1852	77
Rachel Donelson Jackson	1767—1828	61
Hannah Hoes Van Buren	1783—1819	36
Anna Tuthill Symmes Harrison	1775—1864	89
Letitia Christian Tyler	1790—1842	52
Julia Gardiner Tyler	1820—1889	69
Sarah Childress Polk	1803—1891	88
Margaret Mackall Smith Taylor	1788—1852	64
Abigail Powers Fillmore	1798—1853	55
Jane Means Appleton Pierce	1806—1863	57
Harriet Lane	1830—1903	73
Mary Todd Lincoln	1818—1882	64
Eliza McCardle Johnson	1810—1876	66
Julia Dent Grant	1826—1902	76
Lucy Ware Webb Hayes	1831—1889	58
Lucretia Rudolph Garfield	1832—1918	86
Ellen Lewis Herndon Arthur	1837—1880	43
Frances Folsom Cleveland	1864—1947	83
Caroline Lavinia Scott Harrison	1832—1892	60
Ida Saxton McKinley	1847—1907	60
Edith Kermit Carow Roosevelt	1861—1948	87
Helen Herron Taft	1861—1943	82
Ellen Louise Axson Wilson	1860—1914	54
Edith Bolling Galt Wilson	1872—1961	89
Florence Kling Harding	1860—1924	64
Grace Anna Goodhue Coolidge	1879—1957	78
Lou Henry Hoover	1874—1944	70
Anna Eleanor Roosevelt Roosevelt	1884—1962	78
Elizabeth Virginia Wallace Truman	1885—1982	97
Mamie Geneva Doud Eisenhower	1896—1979	83
Jacqueline Lee Bouvier Kennedy Onassis	1929—1994	65
Claudia Taylor Johnson	1912— 2007	94
Patricia Ryan Nixon	1912—1993	81
Elizabeth Bloomer Ford	1918— 2011	93
Rosalynn Smith Carter	1927—	
Nancy Davis Reagan	1923— 2016	95
Barbara Pierce Bush	1925— 2018	92
Hillary Rodham Clinton	1947—	
Laura Welch Bush	1946—	

Histogram Using A Graphing Calculator

STAT → Edit → Clear L1 → enter ages into L1

Graph:

$\boxed{Y=}$ Clear all y-registers

$\boxed{2^{nd}}$ $\boxed{Y=}$ Turn on Plot 1 only

Enter for Plot 1 $\boxed{ON}$

Type $--\ominus---$ enter

x list: L1

Freq: 1

Zoom 9

Window   x min: 30 $\boxed{Graph}$ Trace

                 x max: 100

                 x scale: 10

Histogram

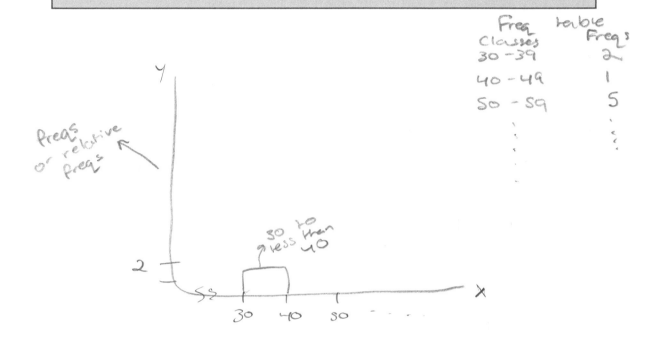

Freq table

Classes	Freqs
30 -39	2
40 - 49	1
50 - 59	5

Freqs or relative freqs

30 to less than 40

Location: Center ≈ 75 or 70s

Spread: 30 to 100 or 34 to 97

Shape: Skewed left/negatively skewed

Outliers: no

Stem-and-Leaf Plot: The stem contains all but the last digit of a number. The leaf is the last digit of the number.

- **Example:** Here are the numbers of home runs that Babe Ruth hit in his 15 years with the New York Yankees:

54, 59, 35, 41, 46, 25, 47, 60, 54,

46, 49, 46, 41, 43, 22

Key: Leaf unit: 1   ones position in raw data

```
2 | 5 2
3 | 5
4 | 1 6 7 6 9 6 1 3
5 | 4 9 4
6 | 0
```

stem   leaves

Min: 22
Max: 60

stem | leaves

Ideally, the range of these numbers should be ≈ 5 or up to ≈ 15

Center ≈ 40.
Spread: 22 to 60
Shape ≈ normal
Outliers: none

Minitab Stem-and-Leaf Plot

Stem-and-Leaf Display: Grades

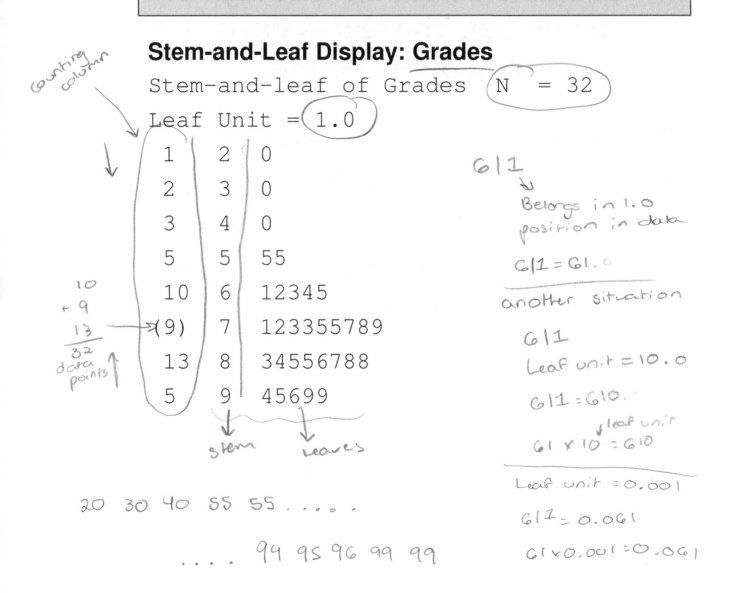

Stem-and-leaf of Grades   N = 32
Leaf Unit = 1.0

```
 1     2   0
 2     3   0
 3     4   0
 5     5   55
10     6   12345
(9)    7   123355789
13     8   34556788
 5     9   45699
```

counting column

10
+ 9
13
32
data points

stem   leaves

20 30 40 55 55 . . . . .

. . . . 94 95 96 99 99

6|1
↳
Belongs in 1.0
position in data

6|1 = 61.0

another situation

6|1
Leaf unit = 10.0

6|1 = 610.

         leaf unit
61 × 10 = 610

Leaf unit = 0.001

6|1 = 0.061

61 × 0.001 = 0.061

Example: Suppose that scores on a quiz for (n = 7) students in a class are: 91, 79, 60, 94, 89, 93, 86

① • Mean: → Average of the data values

$$\frac{\text{Add up data values}}{\text{\# values in dataset}}$$

$$\Sigma(x_i)/n$$
↓ sum   ↘ individual data values

② • Median: Middle value when the data is ordered

Position of the median $\frac{(n+1)}{2}$

③ • Mode: Item or category w/ largest frequency

No formula → simply find item/category that occurs most often

37

Find the Median

1. Order the data

2. If n is odd, the median M is the observation in middle of the ordered values

Ex: 60 79 86 (89) 91 93 94

Rule: Position of med.

$$\frac{n+1}{2} = \frac{7+1}{2} = \frac{8}{2} = 4^{th}$$

3. If n is even, the median M is the average of the two data values in the middle of the ordered values

Ex: 60 79 86 (89 ⸱ 91) 93 94 95

$$\frac{n+1}{2} = \frac{8+1}{2} = \frac{9}{2} = 4.5 \ position$$

$$\frac{89+91}{2} = 90 \ ^{\text{median}}$$

Example: Suppose that scores on a quiz for n = 8 students in a class are: 91, 79, 60, 94, 89, 93, 86, 75

- **Mean:** → sample mean: $\bar{x}$ x-Bar $\boxed{83.375}$

Stat → edit → clear L1 then enter data

Stat → CALC → 1: 1 var stats

List : L1
Freq list: / leave this blank

Calculate.

- **Median:** Med = $\boxed{87.5}$

Ex2: Quiz grades (L1) | 60 | 70 | 80 | 90 | 100 | } Freq table

Quiz grades	60	70	80	90	100
Freqs (L2)	10	18	25	31	7

$\bar{x} = 80.8$ med = 80

- **Mode:** → not on your calculator

90s

→ List: L1
Freqlist: L2

Percentiles: the kth percentile is a number that has k% of the data values at or below it and (100-k)% of the data values at or above it.

Your score on a particular test puts you @ 90ᵗʰ percentile

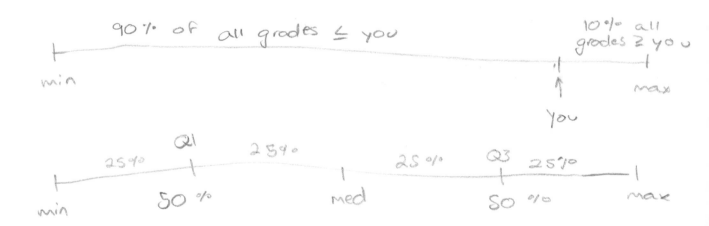

90% of all grades ≤ you   10% all grades ≥ you

min   max

                                                    ↑
                                                   you

25%   Q1   25%   25%   Q3   25%

min   50%   med   50%   max

Finding Quartiles:
Q_1 = lower quartile

Q_3 = upper quartile

- **Example:** Suppose that scores on a quiz for $n = 7$ students in a class are:
91, 79, 60, 94, 89, 93, 86

$$\overset{Q1}{} \qquad \overset{Q3}{}$$

60 (79) 86 (89) 91 (93) 94

1st find Med:

Rule: $\dfrac{n+1}{2} = \dfrac{8}{2} = 4^{th}$

To find Quartiles: # of data points to left/right of Med

Rule: $\dfrac{n_1 + 1}{2}$

Q: $\dfrac{3+1}{2} = 2^{nd}$

Finding Quartiles:

Q_1 = lower quartile

Q_3 = upper quartile

- **Example:** Suppose that scores on a quiz for n = 8 students in a class are: 91, 79, 60, 94, 89, 93, 86, 75

60   75 ⟩79   86 ⟩89   91 ⟩93   94

Med: $\frac{8+1}{2} = 4.5$ position $\frac{86+89}{2} = 87.5$

Q1: $\frac{4+1}{2} = 2.5$ position $\frac{75+79}{2} = 77$

Q3 $\frac{91+93}{2} = 92$

Minitab Stem-and-Leaf Plot

Stem-and-Leaf Display: Grades

```
Stem-and-leaf of Grades    N   = 32
Leaf Unit = 1.0
    1     2   0
    2     3   0
    3     4   0
    5     5   55
   10     6   12345
   (9)    7   123355789
   13     8   34556788
    5     9   45699
```

counter ↙   stem ↓   leaves

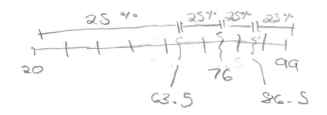

25 %   25% 25% 25%

20   63.5   76   86.5   99

Med: $\frac{32+1}{2} = \frac{33}{2} = 16.5$ $\frac{75+77}{2} = \boxed{76}$

Q_1: $\frac{16+1}{2} = \frac{17}{2} = 8.5$ $\frac{63+64}{2} = \boxed{63.5}$

Q_3: $\frac{86+87}{2} = \boxed{86.5}$

- **Example 2.14:** The weights (in pounds) for nine men of the Cambridge crew team:

  188.5,183, 194.5, 185, 214, 203.5, 186, 178.5, 109

109

178.5

183

185

(186)

188.5

194.5

203.5

214

Med $\frac{9+1}{2} = 5^{th}$

$\frac{4+1}{2} = 2.5$ position

$\frac{178.5+183}{2} = 180.75$

$\frac{194.5+203.5}{2} = 199$

min: 109

Q1 : 180.75

med: 186

Q3: 199

Max: 214

Draw a Boxplot and Identify Outliers

1. Label either a vertical or a horizontal axis with numbers from the minimum to the maximum data values.

2. Draw a box with the lower end of the box at Q_1 and the upper end at Q_3.

3. Draw a line through the box at the median.

4. Calculate the Interquartile Range:

    $$IQR = Q_3 - Q_1 \quad \text{, midrange}$$

5. Find the Lower Fence:

    $$Q_1 - 1.5(IQR)$$

    Find the Upper Fence:

    $$Q_3 + 1.5(IQR)$$

6. The lower whisker is a line that extends from Q_1 to the smallest data value not less than the Lower Fence.

    The upper whisker is a line that extends from Q_3 to the largest data value not greater than the Upper Fence.

7. Data values outside the fences are considered outliers.

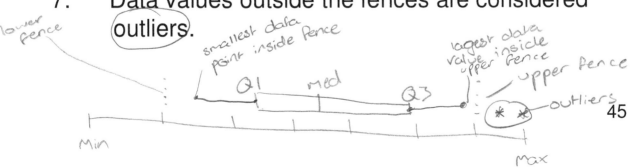

lower fence   smallest data point inside fence   Q1   med   Q3   largest data value inside upper fence   upper fence   outliers

Min   Max

45

(109) (178.5) 183 185 186 188.5 194.5 203.5 (214)

Weights of Cambridge Crew Members

Median		186
Quartiles	180.75	199
Extremes	109	214

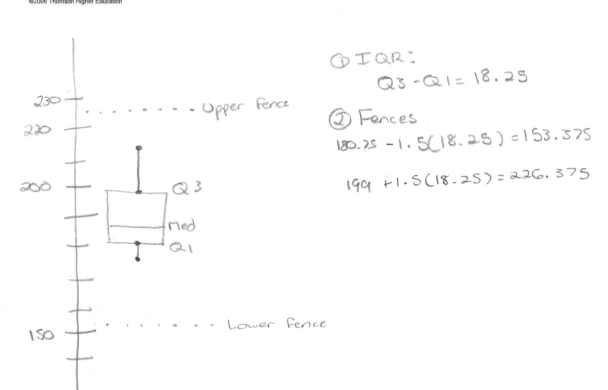

① IQR:
$$Q3 - Q1 = 18.25$$

② Fences
$$180.75 - 1.5(18.25) = 153.375$$

$$199 + 1.5(18.25) = 226.375$$

Addressing Outliers

1. The outlier is a legitimate data value

    Keep it

2. A mistake was made taking a measurement or entering it into the computer

    Correct it

    or discard it

3. The observation in question belongs to a different group than the bulk of data observed

    Crew team: 8 rowers, 1 coxswain

    If your goal: Avg wt. of a rower → discard 109

    If your goal: Avg wt of entire team → keep 109

A Sampling of Increasing Pay For Top Hospital Administrators in CT

enter the #s in thousands

Hospital		2002 Salary (L1)	2006 Salary (L2)
Bridgeport	245	$244,524	$725,480
St. Mary's	239	239,484	498,686
Middlesex		511,220	932,923
Stamford		515,761	887,256
Danbury		418,808	684,522
Backus		341,298	535,883
Norwalk		426,328	646,945
Lawrence		333,114	479,103
New Milford		321,721	462,018
Yale		818,841	1,086,649 → 1087
St. Francis		640,955	824,403
Hartford		811,802	1,037,051
St. Raphael		464,524	561,669

Plot 1   Type - - - ↓ - -

   xlist: L1
   Freq: 1

Plot 2
   xlist: L2
   Freq: 1

A Sampling of Increasing Pay For Top Hospital Administrators in CT

	2002	2006
Min	$239,000	$462,000
Q1	$327,500	$517,500
Med	$426,000	$685,000
Q3	$578,500	$910,000
Max	$819,000	$1,087,000

What salary do 1/4 of all administrators earn <u>more</u> than? $910,000

What salary do 3/4 of all admins earn more than? $517,500

A Sampling of Increasing Pay For Top Hospital Administrators in CT

Calculate % increase in salaries from 2002
to 2006 and store this in L3

STAT → edit → L3
↓
Highlight this
name, L3

press enter

L3 = (L2-L1)/L1 ×100

L1 L2 [L3]

Boxplot of L3

Min   21%

midrange ┌ Q1   31 %

middle
50%   │   Med   52 %

      └ Q3   77 %

Max   196 %

50

Describing Shape

1. Symmetric:

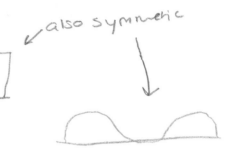

also symmetric

also symmetric

When the data is symmetric, mean ≈ median

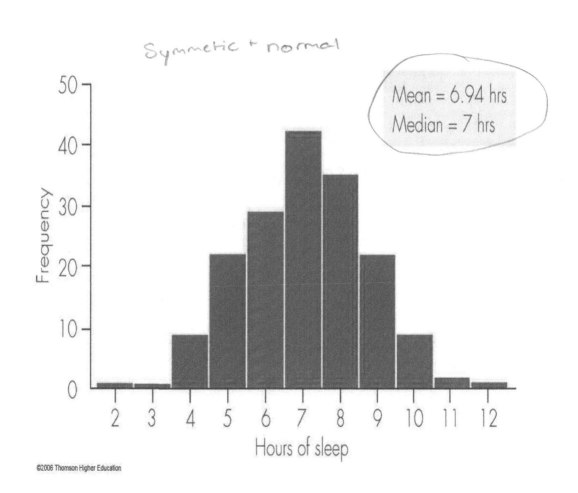

Symmetric + normal

Mean = 6.94 hrs
Median = 7 hrs

©2006 Thomson Higher Education

51

Median is always @ 50 % mark
Not affected by skewness

Describing Shape

2. Skewed to the right: positively Skewed

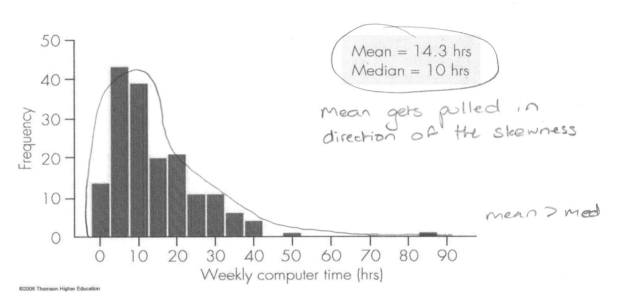

Mean = 14.3 hrs
Median = 10 hrs

Mean gets pulled in
direction of the skewness

mean > med

©2006 Thomson Higher Education

3. Skewed to the left: negatively skewed

mean < med

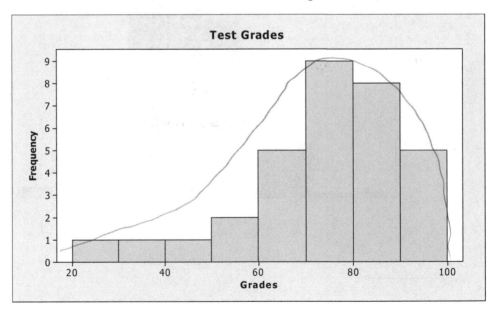

Influence of Shape on the Mean and the Median

Sample of salaries @ UConn
($1000s)

can round or not ↓

064   051   104   53   41   112   157   168   350

72   81   166

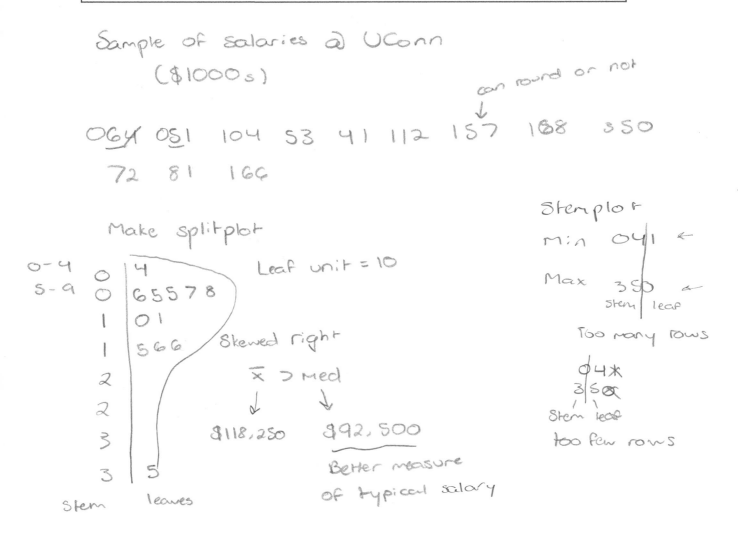

Make splitplot

Leaf unit = 10

```
0-4    0 | 4
5-9    0 | 65578
       1 | 01
       1 | 566      Skewed right
       2 |            x̄ > Med
       2 |              ↓        ↓
       3 |          $118,250   $92,500
       3 | 5                   _____
stem    leaves              Better measure
                            of typical salary
```

Stemplot

Min 041 ←

Max 350 ←
          stem | leaf

Too many rows

```
04*
35α
stem leaf
```
too few rows

53

Two Major Categories of Statistical Techniques

① • **Descriptive Statistics:** → describing our data set graphically + numerically

We can do this for samples + populations

② • **Inferential Statistics:**

We use data we collect to generalize to a larger group

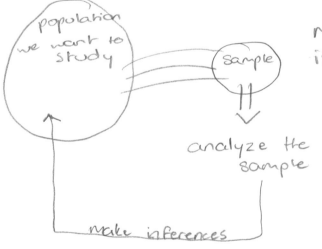

population we want to study

sample

Make sure that sample is good representation of population

analyze the sample

make inferences

Descriptive Statistics and Inferential Statistics

Statistics to estimate parameters

measurements are called parameters

Do all our calculations
measurements are called statistics

population has a mean, called "mu", written μ

$$\mu = \frac{\sum x_i}{n} \rightarrow \text{population size}$$

mean: $\bar{x} = \frac{\sum x_i}{n}$ $\rightarrow$ sample size

x-bar
$=$
$\vee$
sample mean

$\bar{x}$ estimates μ

Numerical Summaries of Quantitative Variables: Spread or Variation or Dispersion

1. Range : Max - min

2. Interquartile Range

   $$IQR = Q3 - Q1$$

3. Standard Deviation

   Start w/ a sample st. dev.

   = "average" deviation of the data around the mean

4. Variance

   (st. deviation)^2

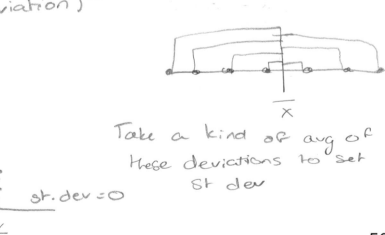

Take a kind of avg of these deviations to set st dev

st. dev = 0

To find an average deviations, you would most likely do this: $\frac{\Sigma(x_i - \bar{x})}{n} = 0 \Rightarrow$ this doesn't work

Calculation of a Sample Standard Deviation

gets rid of negatives

x_i	Deviations $(x_i - \bar{x})$	Squared deviations $(x_i - \bar{x})^2$
20	$20 - 45 = -25$	$(-25)^2 = 625$
30	$30 - 45 = -15$	$(-15)^2 = 225$
40	$40 - 45 = -5$	$(-5)^2 = 25$
50	$50 - 45 = 5$	$(5)^2 = 25$
60	$60 - 45 = 15$	$(15)^2 = 225$
70	$70 - 45 = 25$	$(25)^2 = 625$

sample data

Sample mean $\bar{x} = 45$ variance $n = 6$ $\Sigma(x_i - \bar{x})^2 = 1750$

Sample variance $s^2 = \dfrac{\Sigma(x_i - \bar{x})^2}{n-1} = \dfrac{1750}{5} = 350$

Dividing by n-1 gives an adjusted avg squared deviation

Sample standard deviation $s = \sqrt{\dfrac{\Sigma(x_i - \bar{x})^2}{n-1}} = \sqrt{350} = 18.7$

57

Population Standard Deviation Vs. Sample Standard Deviation

Populations   vs   Samples
$\downarrow$ $\downarrow$

measurements called   measurements called
parameters   statistics

$$\mu = \frac{\sum x_i}{n} \qquad \text{mean} \qquad \bar{x} = \frac{\sum x_i}{n}$$

$\downarrow$

on your
calculator

$\sigma \rightarrow$ small sigma

or $\boxed{\sigma x} \downarrow$ standard s or $\boxed{sx} \downarrow$
deviations

$$\sqrt{\frac{\sum (x_i - \mu)^2}{n}} \qquad\qquad \sqrt{\frac{\sum (x_i - \bar{x})^2}{n-1}}$$

58

Population Standard Deviation
Vs.
Sample Standard Deviation

Why does "s" use n-1 in the denominator rather than n?

Because in statistical inference we want to use "s" to estimate "σ"

"s" is a better estimator of σ w/ n-1 in the denominator

Population

min   max

you collect a sample

The sample probably varies a little bit less than the population

We "adjust" the sample st dev and make it a little bit bigger by using n-1 in the denominator instead of n

Formulas for Standard Deviation and Variance

σ^2 = Population Variance = $\dfrac{\sum(x_i - \mu)^2}{N}$

σ = Population Standard Deviation = $\sqrt{\dfrac{\sum(x_i - \mu)^2}{N}}$

Sigma → σx

s^2 = Sample Variance = $\dfrac{\sum(x_i - \bar{x})^2}{n-1}$

s = Sample Standard Deviation = $\sqrt{\dfrac{\sum(x_i - \bar{x})^2}{n-1}}$

sx

Quiz data for a sample of students

60   75   79   86   89   91   93   94 ← L1

Calc: $\bar{x} = 83.575$ $sx = 11.575$

Quiz data for a sample of students

L1	70	75	80	85	90	95	100
L2	4	6	8	11	13	3	1

$\bar{x} = 83.913$ $sx = 7.447$

60

Goal: use sample info to describe a population

Features of Bell-Shaped (normal) Distributions

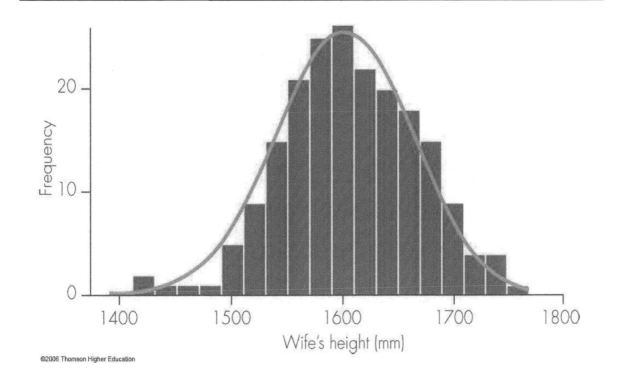

Wife's height (mm)

©2006 Thomson Higher Education

Data: sample of heights of women in England

Sample info $\begin{cases} \bar{x} = 1602 \text{ mm } (\approx 63" \text{ tall}) \\ S = S_x = 62.4 \text{ mm} \\ \text{Graph: Histogram} \end{cases}$

↓

generalize to population → estimate mu = 1602 mm

" σ = 62.4 mm

Shape ≈ normal

describes population in more detail

The Empirical Rule states that for any bell-shaped curve, approximately

only for data that is ≈ normal

- **68%** of the values fall within **1** standard deviation of the mean

- **95%** of the values fall within **2** standard deviations of the mean

- **99.7%** (almost 100%) of the values fall within **3** standard deviations of the mean

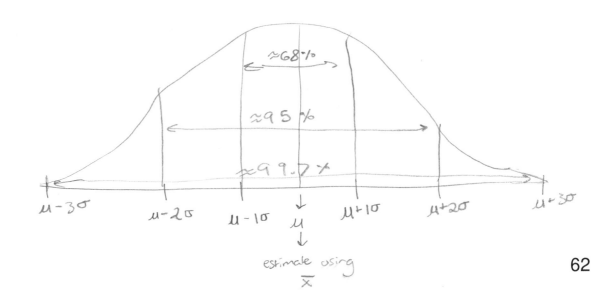

≈68%

≈95%

≈99.7%

$\mu - 3\sigma$ $\mu - 2\sigma$ $\mu - 1\sigma$ μ $\mu + 1\sigma$ $\mu + 2\sigma$ $\mu + 3\sigma$

estimate using $\bar{x}$

Women's Heights and the Empirical Rule

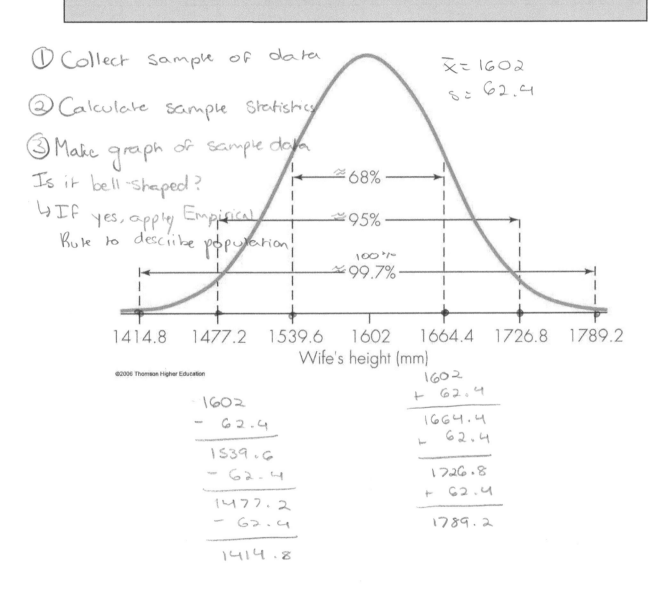

① Collect sample of data

② Calculate sample statistics

③ Make graph of sample data

Is it bell-shaped?

↳ If yes, apply Empirical Rule to describe population

$\bar{x} = 1602$
$s = 62.4$

≈68%
≈95%
100%
≈99.7%

1414.8   1477.2   1539.6   1602   1664.4   1726.8   1789.2

Wife's height (mm)

©2006 Thomson Higher Education

```
  1602
-  62.4
───────
1539.6
-  62.4
───────
1477.2
-  62.4
───────
1414.8
```

```
  1602
+  62.4
───────
1664.4
+  62.4
───────
1726.8
+  62.4
───────
1789.2
```

63

Women's Heights and the Empirical Rule

Make sure your data is normal in shape

generalize from the sample to the population

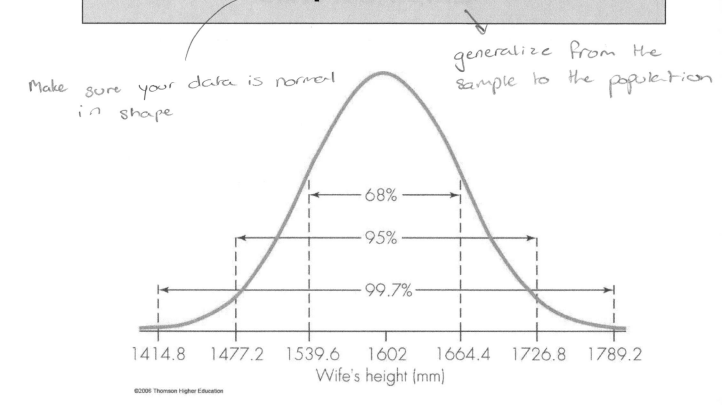

68%

95%

99.7%

1414.8   1477.2   1539.6   1602   1664.4   1726.8   1789.2

Wife's height (mm)

©2006 Thomson Higher Education

95 %
− 68 %
27 %/2

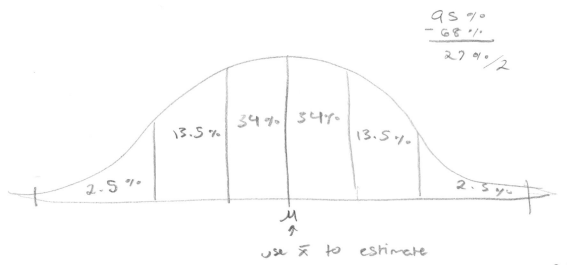

2.5 %   13.5 %   34%   34%   13.5 %   2.5 %

μ

use x̄ to estimate

Example: Waist circumferences of adult females have a bell-shaped distribution with a mean of 36 in. and a standard deviation of 3.5 in.

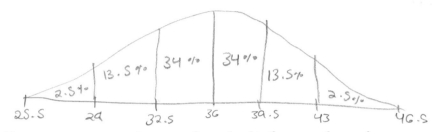

1. What proportion of adult females have a waist circumference between 32.5 and 39.5 in?

    68 %

2. between 29 and 39.5 in?

    13.5 % + 34% + 34 % = 81.5 %

3. less than 32.5 in?

    13.5% + 2.5% = 16 %

4. greater than 32.5 in?

    84 %

Entering Data into a Table on TI Calculator

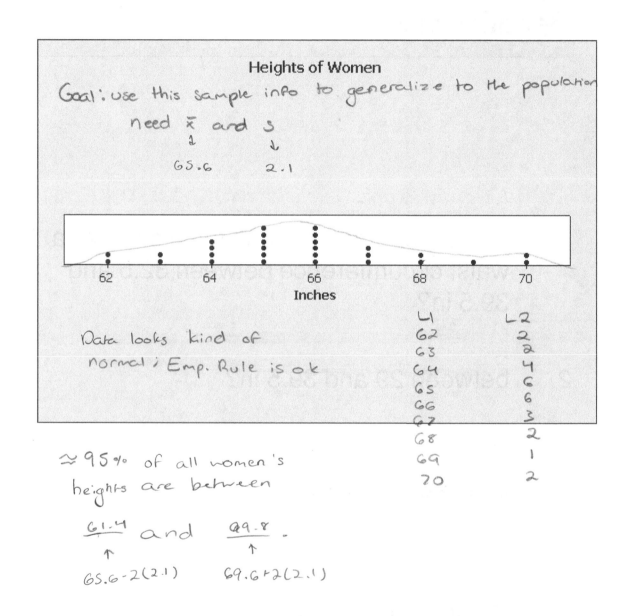

Heights of Women

Goal: use this sample info to generalize to the population

need $\bar{x}$ and s

65.6   2.1

62   64   66   68   70

Inches

Data looks kind of
normal; Emp. Rule is ok

L1	L2
62	2
63	2
64	4
65	6
66	6
67	3
68	2
69	1
70	2

≈ 95% of all women's
heights are between

61.4 and 69.8 .

65.6 - 2(2.1)   69.6 + 2(2.1)

The Empirical Rule, the Standard Deviation and the Range

Large sample
of data

min = 75

max = 128

Shape is normal

estimate $\mu = \dfrac{min + max}{2} = 101.5$

estimate $\sigma = \dfrac{max - min}{6} = 8.83$

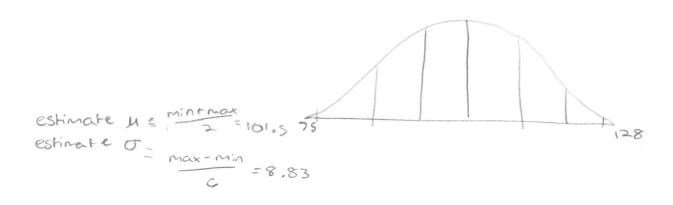

75

128

2 to 20 years: Boys
Stature-for-age and Weight-for-age percentiles

NAME _____

RECORD # _____

Mother's Stature		Father's Stature		
Date	Age	Weight	Stature	BMI*

*To Calculate BMI: Weight (kg) ÷ Stature (cm) ÷ Stature (cm) x 10,000
or Weight (lb) ÷ Stature (in) ÷ Stature (in) x 703

AGE (YEARS)

12 13 14 15 16 17 18 19 20

STATURE

WEIGHT

AGE (YEARS)

2 3 4 5 6 7 8 9 10 11 12 13 14 15 16 17 18 19 20

Published May 30, 2000 (modified 11/21/00).
SOURCE: Developed by the National Center for Health Statistics in collaboration with

The Empirical Rule, the Standard Deviation and the Range

Boys: 12 years old
   Heights

From the chart:

   50% → estimate
      $\mu \approx 58.5"$

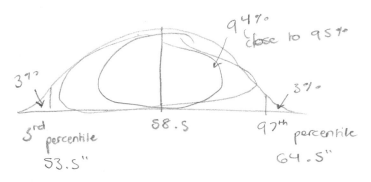

Empirical Rule says $\approx 95\%$ of population lies in interval
      $\mu \pm 2\sigma$

estimate σ : $\dfrac{\left(\begin{array}{c} \text{upper edge of} \\ 95\% \text{ interval} \end{array} - \begin{array}{c} \text{lower edge of} \\ 95\% \text{ interval} \end{array} \right)}{4}$

      $\sigma \approx 2.75$

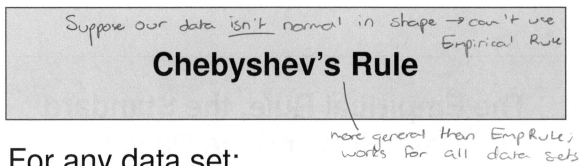

Suppose our data _isn't_ normal in shape → can't use Empirical Rule

Chebyshev's Rule

more general than Emp Rule; works for all data sets

For any data set:

At least 75% of the data will lie within 2 standard deviations of the mean

At least 89% of the data will lie within 3 standard deviations of the mean

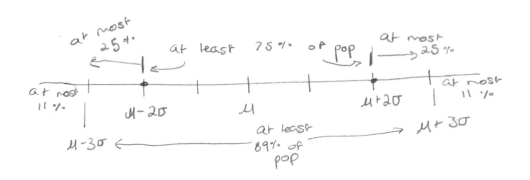

Example: In a telephone survey 590 randomly selected individuals were asked, "What is the maximum number of years you expect to spend with any one employer?" The <u>mean</u> of the responses was 1<u>0 ye</u>ars and the <u>standard deviation</u> was 3 years. The data was sk<u>ewed</u> to the right.

Chebychev's rule

1. Approximately what proportion of responses would you expect to be between 4 and 16 years?

75 %

2. Approximately what proportion of responses would you expect to be more than 19 years?

11 %

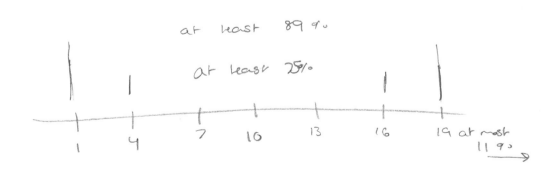

at least 89 %

at least 25 %

4   7   10   13   16   19 at most 11 %

Patriots Salaries: → μ

Population mean: $2,001,935

Population standard deviation: $2,811,328 → σ

1. At least 75% of the players

make between ___ and ___
↓ negative #   ↑ μ+2σ   earn $7.6 mil
                              or less

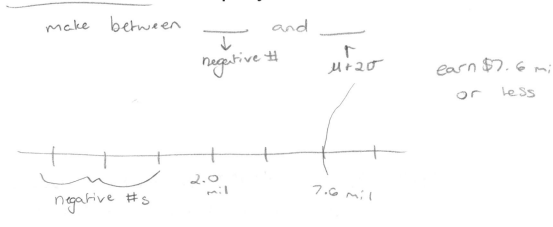

negative #s   2.0 mil   7.6 mil

2. At least 89% of the players make:

$10.4 mil or less

Entering Data into a Table on TI Calculator

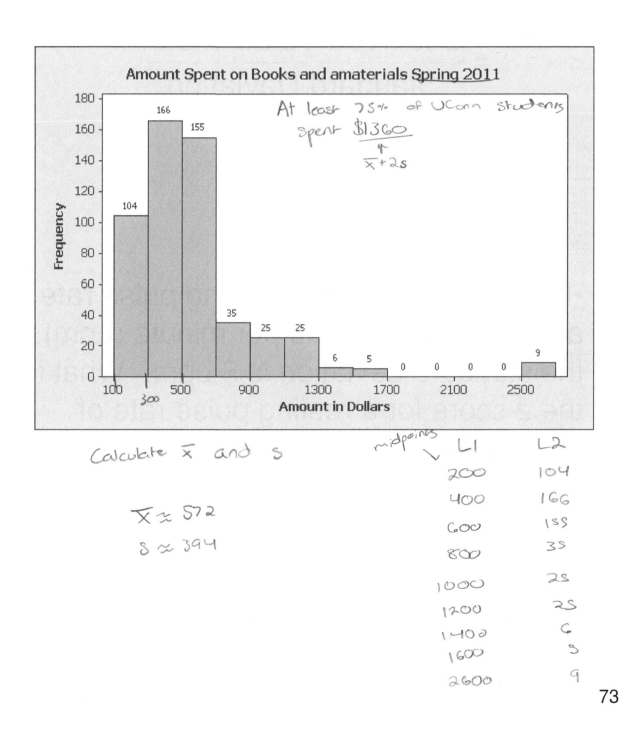

Amount Spent on Books and amaterials Spring 2011

At least 75% of UConn students spent $1360

$$\frac{}{\overline{x}+2s}$$

Calculate $\overline{x}$ and s

midpoints

$\overline{x} \approx 572$

$s \approx 394$

L1	L2
200	104
400	166
600	155
800	35
1000	25
1200	25
1400	6
1600	5
2600	9

Standardized Score or *z*-Score is a useful measure of the relative standing of any observation in a dataset

$$z = \frac{\text{Observed Value} - \text{Mean}}{\text{Standard Deviation}}$$

Formula:

$$z = \frac{x - \bar{x}}{s} \quad \text{or} \quad z = \frac{x - \mu}{\sigma}$$

•**Example:** The mean resting pulse rate for adult men is 70 beats per minute (bpm), the standard deviation is 8 bpm. What is the *z*-score for a resting pulse rate of 80 bpm?

one observed value

$$z = \frac{80 - 70}{8} = 1.25$$

This means that an observed value of 80 is 1.25 standard deviations above the mean

2nd method for determining whether a data point is an outlier

The Empirical Rule for bell-shaped data can be restated as follows:

• Approximately 68% of values have *z*-scores between -1 and +1

• Approximately 95% of values have z-scores between -2 and +2

• Approximately 99.7% (almost 100%) of values have *z*-scores between -3 and +3

If z-score is >3 or < -3, the data point is an outlier

Technical note:
To perfectly match 1.5IQR rule for outliers, we would need to use cutoffs of z >2.7 or z <-2.7 for outliers

We rounded to 3 and -3 for simplicity

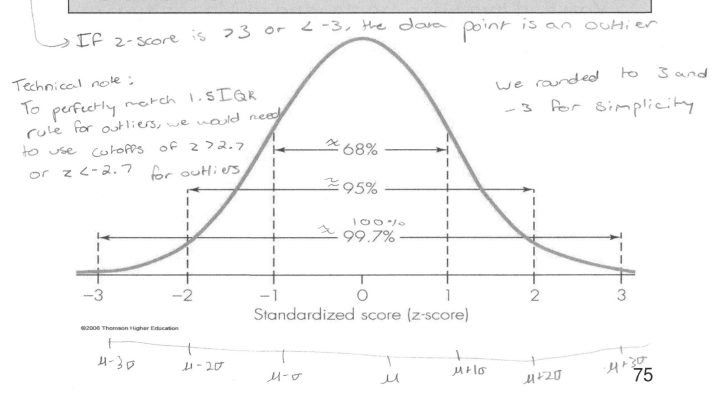

Standardized score (z-score)

$\mu - 3\sigma$ $\mu - 2\sigma$ $\mu - \sigma$ μ $\mu + 1\sigma$ $\mu + 2\sigma$ $\mu + 3\sigma$

z-Score as a measure of relative standing

- **Example:**

Monthly Rent in Manhattan:

$$z = \frac{(2511.10 - 2016.50)}{294.6}$$

$\mu = \$2016.50$
$\sigma = \$294.60$

$$z = 1.68$$

Monthly Rent in Hartford:

$\mu = \$1042.50$
$\sigma = \$152.25$

You find two apartments, one in Manhattan, one in Hartford.

Manhattan Rent: $2511.10

Hartford Rent: $1436.55

$$z = \frac{(1436.55 - 1042.5)}{152.25}$$

$$z = 2.59$$

Which apartment is more expensive, relatively speaking?   Hartford

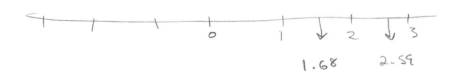

Chapter 3
Relationships Between Quantitative Variables

- ## Are ②quantitative variables related? If so, how?

Ex: SAT $\overset{x}{scores}$ + GPAs in $\overset{y}{college}$

Can we use SAT scores to predict GPAs in college?

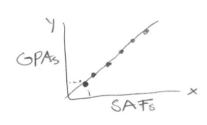

All the points sit directly on a mathematical function (in this case, it's a line): deterministic model

We have a scatter of points around a math. function = probabalistic model

w/ this much scatter, SATs are no longer good predictors of GPAs

A Relationship between two Quantitative Variables

3 topics in Ch. 3

① • Scatterplot: – What pattern exists between x_s and y_s?

→ Sine model
$y = a \sin(bx + c)$
need $a, b,$ and c

② • Regression Equation:

→ Linear model
$y = mx + b$

Slope = $\dfrac{\text{Change in } y}{\text{Change in } x}$

y-intercept! where line crosses y-axis

→ Quadratic model
$y = ax^2 + bx + c$
need values for $a, b,$ and c

③ Summary statistics

• Correlation: → "r" → measures how strong linear relationship b/t x and y is

• Coefficient of determination: "R^2" → tells us for any model how much the variation in y_s can be explained by the x_s

82

Identifying Variables

- ## Explanatory Variable: goes on x-axis
  or independent variable
      predictor variable

- ## Response Variable: goes on y-axis
  or dependent "
      predicted "

  Ex: SAT score + GPA in college
         x   y

  Ex: Husband's salary + wife's salary
          x   y
          y   or   x

83

Describing the Relationship between two Quantitative Variables

- **Positive Association:** $x\uparrow, y\uparrow$

- **Negative Association:** $x\uparrow, y\downarrow$

No association

- **Linear Relationship:**

Is it?
or do we need a more complicated model?

Driver Age and Maximum Legibility Distance of Highway Signs

Table 5.2 Data Values for Example 5.2

Age (years)	Distance (feet)	Age	Distance	Age	Distance
18	510	37	420	68	300
20	590	41	460	70	390
22	560	46	450	71	320
23	510	49	380	72	370
23	460	53	460	73	280
25	490	55	420	74	420
27	560	63	350	75	460
28	510	65	420	77	360
29	460	66	300	79	310
32	410	67	410	82	360

Driver Age and Maximum Legibility Distance of Highway Signs

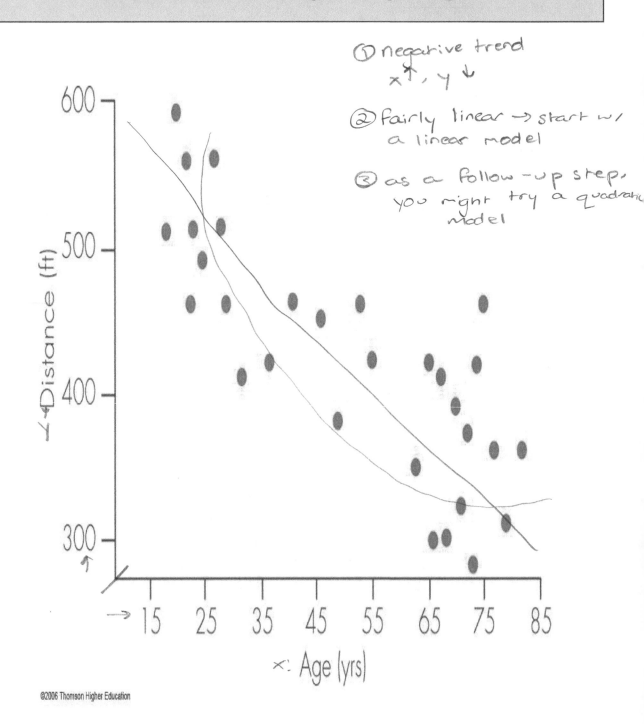

① negative trend
x↑, y↓

② fairly linear → start w/
a linear model

③ as a follow-up step,
you might try a quadratic
model

A Relationship that is Curvilinear

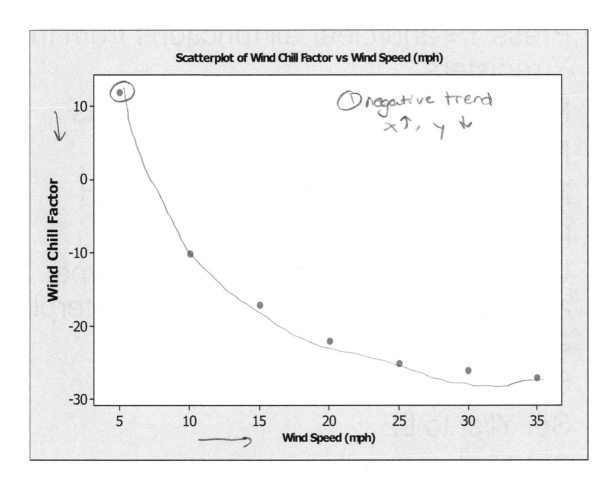

Scatterplot of Wind Chill Factor vs Wind Speed (mph)

① negative trend
x↑, y↓

Clearly not linear
Start w/ curved model
- Quadratic
- Log
- Exponential

Constructing a Scatterplot
Using the TI-83/84

- Press Y= and clear all functions from the Y registers
- Press 2nd Y= to access the StatPlots
- Press Enter to select 1: Plot1
- Move the cursor to highlight On and press ENTER
- Use the Down Arrow to Scroll to Type: and highlight the first icon, the scatterplot and press ENTER
- Scroll to Xlist and set it to L1
- Set Ylist to L2
- Set Mark to the first icon
- Press ZOOM and scroll to 9:ZoomStat
- Press ENTER and the graph will be displayed

If a scatterplot suggests a relationship b/t x and y, what is it?

Regression Analysis

- Examine and quantify the relationship between a quantitative response variable y and one or more explanatory variables x

- Regression equation: describes how, on average, the response variable is related to the explanatory variables y x

- The simplest kind of relationship between two variables is a straight line: **Simple Linear Regression**

Eq: $y = \overset{slope}{m}x + \underset{y-intercept}{b}$

$y = mx + b$

Equation for the Fitted Regression Line

set of data values $\longrightarrow$ x_1, y_1 x_i, y_i
$\qquad\qquad\qquad\qquad\qquad\qquad x_2, y_2$

y: response variable

x: explanatory variable

$\hat{y} = b_0 + b_1 x$

y-hat

$\rightarrow$ prediction equation $\rightarrow$ predicts an average y-value
for a given x-value

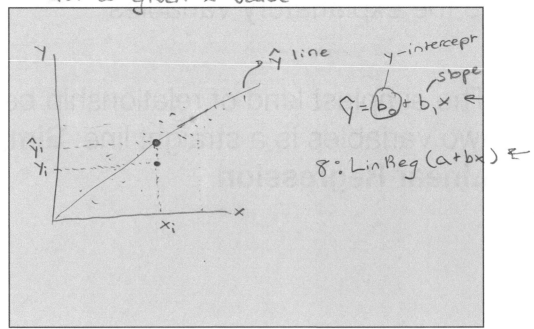

$\hat{y}$ line

y-intercept

slope

$\hat{y} = b_0 + b_1 x$

$8: \text{LinReg}(a+bx)$

Example: In the following dataset, the explanatory variable is 'child's age in years' and the response variable is 'number of words in child's vocabulary'

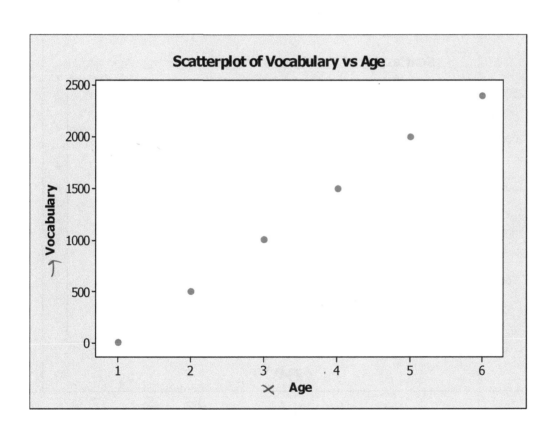

Scatterplot with Regression Line

Create my linear regression equation

Step 1: pick 2 points

Step 2: find slope $\dfrac{y_2 - y_1}{x_2 - x_1} = \dfrac{2000 - 500}{5 - 2} = 500$

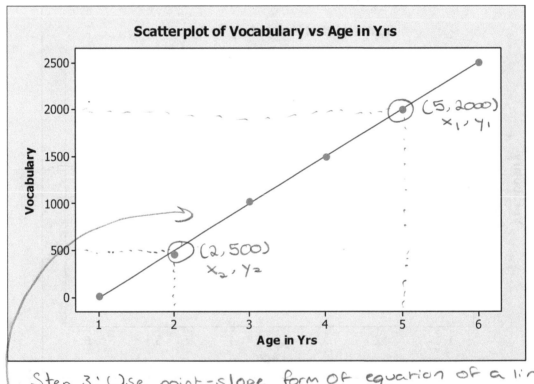

Scatterplot of Vocabulary vs Age in Yrs

(5, 2000)
x_1, y_1

(2, 500)
x_2, y_2

Step 3: Use point-slope form of equation of a line

$y - y_1 = m(x - x_1)$

$y - 500 = 500(x - 2)$

$y - 500 = 500x - 1000$

$y = 500x - 500$

$y = -500 + 500x$

Equation for the Fitted Regression Line

Age	Vocab
1	10
2	500
3	1000
4	1500
5	2000
6	2400

① Enter the data into L1 and L2

② Draw the scatterplot

③ Stat → calc → 8

$y = a + bx$

$a = -460 \quad b = 484.3$

$r =$

$r^2 =$

$\hat{y} = -460 + 484.3x$

Compare this to what we did on previous page algebraically

$\tilde{y} = -500 + 500x$

Initialize your calculator

- This initial step sets up the calculator output to include the correlation value, r. Note: You only need to do this step one time. The setup will be saved for future use

- Press 2nd and the '0' key

- Scroll through the alphabetical listings until you find DIAGNOSTIC ON

- Press ENTER twice and the set up is complete

- Press STAT. Press ENTER to select 1:Edit

- Move the cursor to the top of L1 so that 'L1' is highlighted. Press CLEAR and ENTER

- Repeat the process to CLEAR L2

Finding
the Least Squares Regression Line
Using the TI-83/84

- Enter the x-values into L1 and the y-values into L2
- Set up Plot1 for the Scatterplot
- Press STAT and move the cursor to CALC
- Scroll to 8:LinReg(a+bx) and press ENTER
- **Using STAT WIZARD:**
- Xlist: L1
- Ylist: L2
- FreqList: Note: This must be blank
- Store RegEQ: Vars > Y-Vars > Function> Y1
- Scroll to Calculate and Press Enter to see the regression results
- Press Zoom and press '9' to see the graph

Finding
the Least Squares Regression Line
Using the TI-83/84

- **Without STAT WIZARD:**

- With the cursor flashing next to LinReg(a+bx), press 2nd and '1' followed by a comma. Press 2nd and '2' followed by a comma. Press VARS, move the cursor to Y-VARS, press ENTER to select 1:Function and press ENTER to select Y1

- Press ENTER to see the regression results

- Press Zoom and press '9' to see the graph

Driver Age and Maximum Legibility Distance of Highway Signs

Table 5.2 Data Values for Example 5.2

Age (X)	Distance (Y)	Age	Distance	Age	Distance
18	510	37	420	68	300
20	590	41	460	70	390
22	560	46	450	71	320
23	510	49	380	72	370
23	460	53	460	73	280
25	490	55	420	74	420
27	560	63	350	75	460
28	510	65	420	77	360
29	460	66	300	79	310
32	410	67	410	82	360

Driver Age and Maximum Legibility Distance of Highway Signs

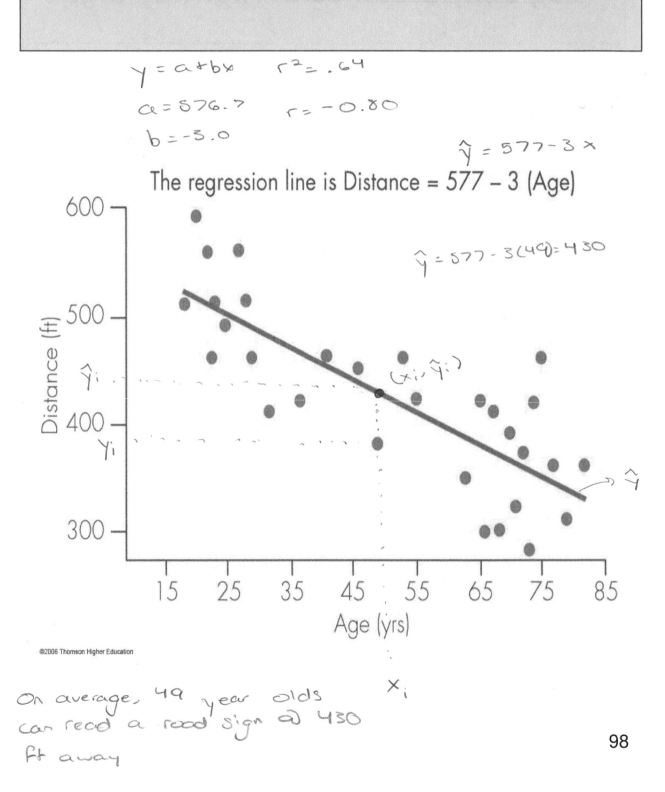

$y = a + bx$ $r^2 = .64$

$a = 576.7$ $r = -0.80$

$b = -3.0$

$\hat{y} = 577 - 3x$

The regression line is Distance = 577 − 3 (Age)

$\hat{y} = 577 - 3(49) = 430$

Distance (ft)

$\hat{y}_i$

y_i

$(x_i, \hat{y}_i)$

$\hat{y}$

600

500

400

300

15   25   35   45   55   65   75   85

Age (yrs)

x_i

On average, 49 year olds
can read a road sign @ 430
ft away

98

The Slope and Intercept of the Regression Line

Linear model:

8: Lin Reg (a+bx) → $\hat{y} = a+bx$

predicted average y-value for a given x-value

y-int   slope

4: Lin Reg (b +ax)

On previous pg: $\hat{y} = 577 - 3x$

This tells you when $x=0$, $\hat{y} = 577$

It may happen that the y-int is well outside the range of x-values

y-int may have no practical meaning within context of the scenario

Slope: "b" → $\dfrac{\text{change in } y}{\text{change in } x}$

↓ always important → tells you how $\hat{y}$ behaves in relationsip to x

In our example, $b = -3 \Rightarrow \dfrac{-3 \to \hat{y}}{1 \to x}$

For every one year increase in age, avg distance decreases by 3 ft

Using the Regression Line for Prediction

predicts an average y-value for a given x-value

$$\hat{y} = 577 - 3x$$

Age	Average Distance
20	$577 - 3(20) = 517$ feet
50	$577 - 3(50) = 427$ feet
80	$577 - 3(80) = 337$ feet

$\hat{y}$

When using the prediction equation, we should restrict x-values so they stay approx within the range of x-values in our data

100

Creating Predicted Values

① Creating predicted $\hat{y}$'s for all values of x in L1

   1st create regression equation using data stored in L1 and L2 and storing it in Y1

   Stat → edit → highlight name "L3" + enter

   $$Y1(L1)$$

   ⌐ x-values

② Creating a predicted value for an x-value not in L1 but in the approx range of L1 values

   Homescreen

   Suppose we want $\hat{y}$ for x=26

   $$Y1(26) = 498 \text{ ft}$$

The observed y-value, the predicted y-value and the residual

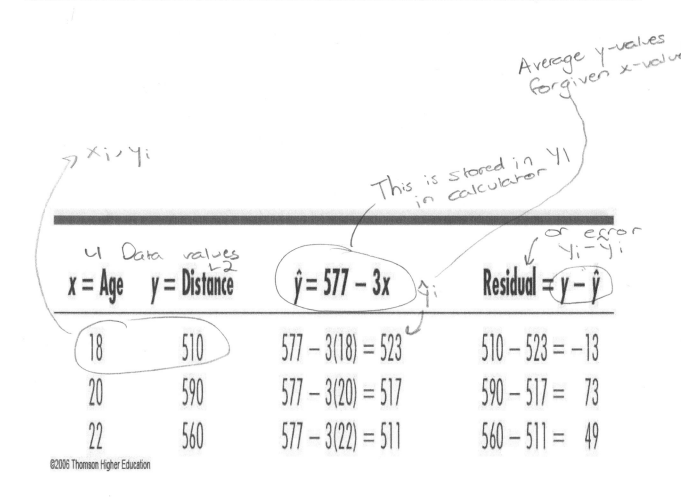

Average y-values for given x-value

→ x_i , y_i

This is stored in Y1 in calculator

4 Data values
L2

or error
$y_i - \hat{y}_i$

x = Age	y = Distance	$\hat{y} = 577 - 3x$	Residual = $y - \hat{y}$
18	510	$577 - 3(18) = 523$	$510 - 523 = -13$
20	590	$577 - 3(20) = 517$	$590 - 517 = 73$
22	560	$577 - 3(22) = 511$	$560 - 511 = 49$

$\hat{y}_i$

@2006 Thomson Higher Education

① Put data into L1 and L2

② Scatterplot → fairly linear ☺

③ Stat → calc → 8 : LinReg(a+bx)
Zoom9

④ Stat → edit → highlight name "L3"
L3 = Y1(L1)

102

Driver Age and Maximum Legibility Distance of Highway Signs

Residual analysis : looking at our linear model that we selected in detail

For a good model, one important criteria is that the residuals should be scattered fairly evenly around the model

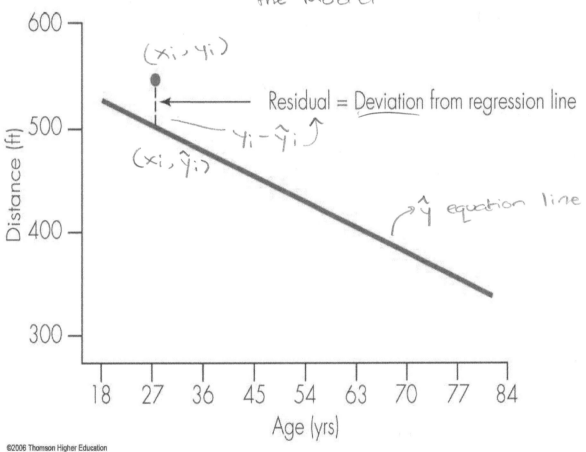

(x_i, y_i)

Residual = <u>Deviation</u> from regression line

$y_i - \hat{y}_i$ ↑

$(x_i, \hat{y}_i)$

$\hat{y}$ equation line

Creating and Graphing Residuals

① After doing the regression, create a column of residuals

Stat → edit → highlight "L4" enter
2nd → Stat → pick Resid enter

| L1 | L2 | L3 | L4 |
| x_s | y_s | $\hat{y}_s$ | Resids |

② Scatterplot of x_s vs. resids
L1   L4

If this plot looks like a scatter (no pattern) of points, that tells us our model is a correct model for the data

If there is a pattern ∴ that tells us our model selection is incorrect + we need to look at other models

Step 1: Deselect Y1

Step 2: 2nd → y= → Plot 1 → change y-list to L4 → Zoom 9

The 'Least Squares' Regression Line

Best fit line through data is line that minimizes $\sum (\text{residuals})^2$

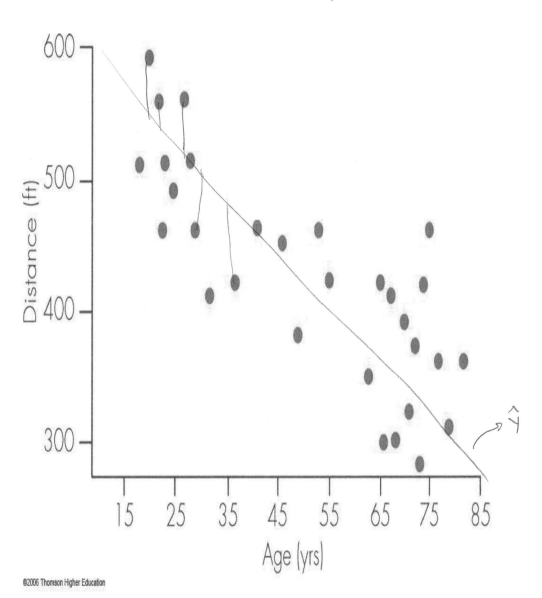

Minitab Regression Output

Minitab Regression Output

Measuring Strength and Direction with Correlation

in a linear model

vs

Calculate "r" → linear correlation coefficient

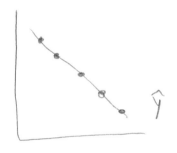

As x↑, y↓
Perfect negative linear correlation
r = -1

As x↑, y↑
Perfect positive linear correlation
r = 1

As x↑, y = ?
No trend
r = 0

r:

A Formula for Sample Correlation

$$r = \frac{1}{n-1} \sum \frac{(x_i - \bar{x})}{s_x} \times \frac{(y_i - \bar{y})}{s_y}$$

standarizing xs

Standardizing ys

Exam 1 Score	Exam 2 Score
70	75
75	82
80	80
80	86
85	90
90	91

Everything gets put on a standardized scale

Makes "r" a scaleless measurement

in   lb
Suppose you study heights vs. weights

Another study of these individuals uses cm and kg

r-value would be same in both scenarios

Do linear reg model

$\hat{y} = 20 + .8x$

$r = .917$

Let's divide all data by 10

$\hat{y} = 2 + .8x$

$r = .917$

A Formula for Sample Correlation

$$r = \frac{1}{n-1} \sum \frac{(x_i - \bar{x})}{s_x} \times \frac{(y_i - \bar{y})}{s_y}$$

Exam1	Exam2		
70	75		
75	82		
80	80		
80	86		
85	90		
90	91		

Correlation

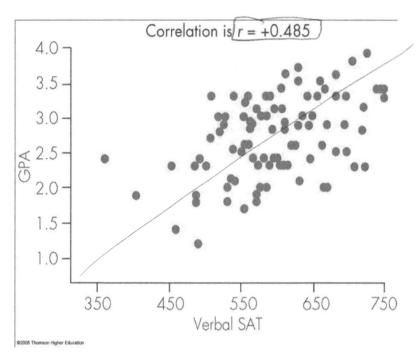

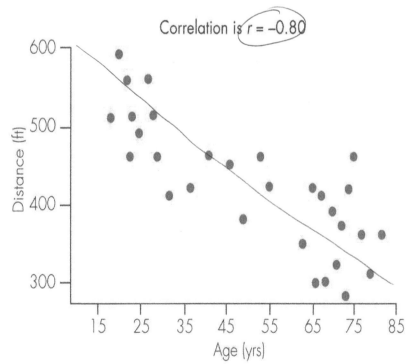

Correlation

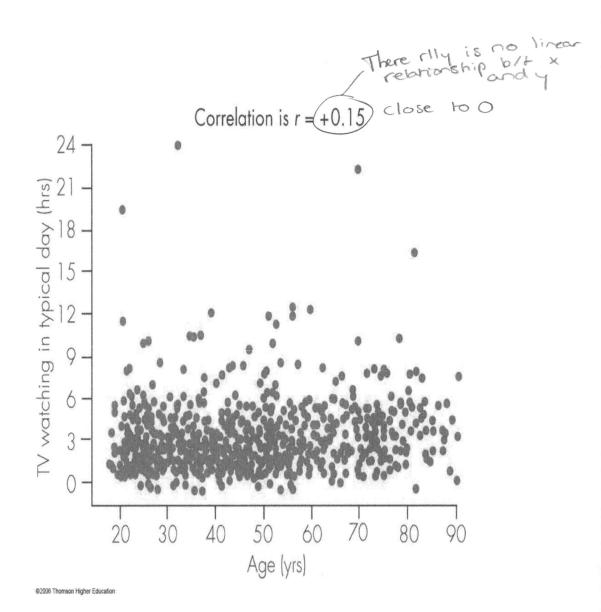

There rlly is no linear relationship b/t x and y

Correlation is r = +0.15   close to 0

©2006 Thomson Higher Education

Correlation Measures the Strength of a Linear Relationship

- Consider the following data set:

X	Y
-5	25
-3	9
-2	4
0	0
2	4
3	9
5	25

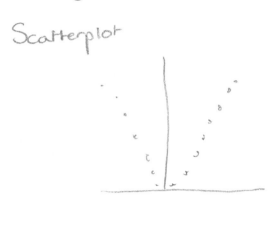

Scatterplot

- Draw the scatterplot and calculate r

Find r: r=0 → there is no linear relationship b/t x and y

What does r=0 mean?

It could mean there's no relationship at all b/t x and y

It could mean x and y are related, but not in a linear fashion

113

Equation for the Fitted Regression Line

Exam grades

1	2
70	75
75	82
80	80
80	86
85	90
90	91

$\downarrow$ $\downarrow$

$\bar{x} = 80$ $\bar{y} = 84$

$S_x = 7.0711$ $S_y = 6.1644$

A scatterplot suggests a linear relationship

$$y : \text{response variable}$$

$$x : \text{explanatory variable}$$

$$\hat{y} = b_0 + b_1 x$$

$\hat{y} = 20 + 0.8x$

$r = .91766$

$$\text{Slope} = b_1 = r \frac{S_y}{S_x} = .91766 \left(\frac{6.1644}{7.0711} \right)$$

$$\text{y-int} = b_0 = \bar{y} - b_1 \bar{x}$$

$84 - .8(80) = 20$

114

Interpreting the Squared Correlation

R^2: → for any model (linear or otherwise)

Tells you how much of the variation in ys can be explained by xs

As decimal or percent → the closer to 1 (or 100%) the better

In linear model we also get r
A measure of the strength of the linear relationship b/t x only

r: closer to +1 or −1 → stronger linear relationship

In linear model, r and r^2 are related
   Relationship $R^2 = r^2$

On calc, r^2 for R^2

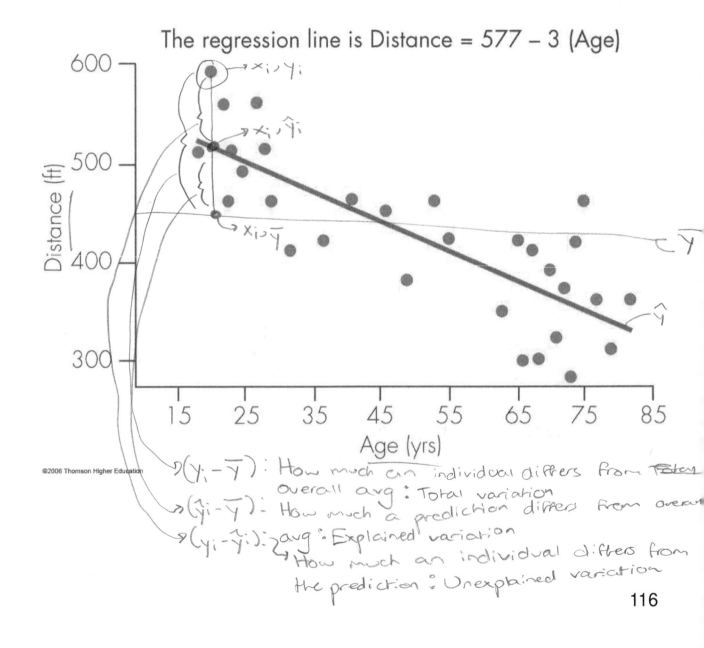

Explained Error and Unexplained Error

Variation

Suppose I want to estimate avg GPA in college for different heights of students

Variation

GPA | height

The regression line is Distance = 577 − 3 (Age)

x_i, y_i

$x_i, \hat{y}_i$

$x_i, \bar{y}$

$\bar{y}$

$\hat{y}$

Distance (ft)

Age (yrs)

©2006 Thomson Higher Education

$(y_i - \bar{y})$: How much an individual differs from overall avg : Total variation

$(\hat{y}_i - \bar{y})$: How much a prediction differs from overall avg : Explained variation

$(y_i - \hat{y}_i)$: How much an individual differs from the prediction : Unexplained variation

116

Explained Error and Unexplained Error

Variation (above "Error")

Variation (below "Error")

$$\sum (y_i - \bar{y})^2$$

$$(\text{Total variation})^2 = SST \quad \rightarrow \text{sum of squares total}$$

$$= \sum (\hat{y}_i - \bar{y})^2$$

$$(\text{explained variation})^2 = SSR \rightarrow \text{sum of squares due to regression model}$$

$$+ \sum (y_i - \hat{y}_i)^2$$

$$(\text{unexplained variation})^2 = SSE \rightarrow \text{sum of squares error}$$

$$SST = SSR + SSE$$

The statistic we get is $r^2 = \dfrac{SSR}{SST} \rightarrow$ proportion of variation in y_s that is explained by x_s

Coefficient of determination
decimal or percent

Regression and Correlation Difficulties and Remedies

- Extrapolating too far beyond the observed range of x-values

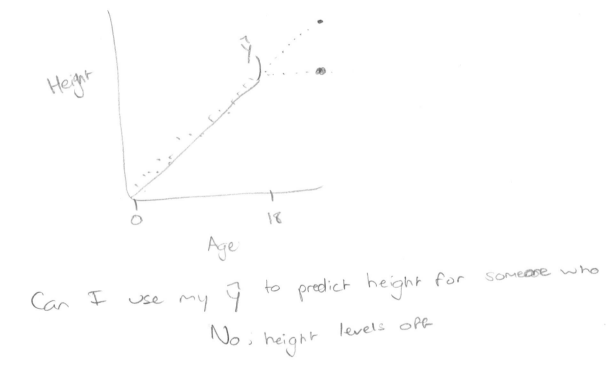

Can I use my $\hat{y}$ to predict height for someone who is 55?

No, height levels off

Should I use mag to predict death? No

- ## Influence of Outliers !!

Major Earthquakes in U.S.: 1850-2009

Output!

Slope: 63.6 =

$$\frac{63.6}{1}$$

As $x \uparrow 1$, $y \uparrow$
63.6

For every additional 1 point in mag, # of deaths ↑ by ≈64

r^2

.055

5.5% of variation can be explained by mag

L1

L2

$\hat{y} = -380 + 63.6x$

$r^2 = .055$

5.5%

$r = .23$

Magnitude	Deaths
7.9	1
6.8	30
7.4	27
6.6	60
7.8	503
6.2	115
7.1	9
7.1	8
7.3	12
7.3	28
6.6	65
6.9	62
7.3	3
6.7	60

r

.23

weak linear relationship

Regression and Correlation: Difficulties and Remedies

- ## Influence of Outliers

Major Earthquakes in U.S.: 1850-2009

I have one outlier (7.8, 503) → remove this from the data

$\hat{y} = 493 - 65x$

$r^2 = .74$

$r = -.86$ } ☺

Slope: $-65 = \boxed{\dfrac{-65}{1}}$

As $x\uparrow$, $y\downarrow$

↳ Weird negative slope

Something else must be affecting the data

① Maybe # of deaths depends on location

② Maybe year in which earthquake occurred has effect on # of deaths

Regression and Correlation: Difficulties and Remedies

- Using correlation and a straight-line regression to describe curvilinear data

Interpret the Slope

$\frac{1.36}{1}$ Every year, the population ↑ by 1.36 mil

multiply by 10

$\frac{13.6}{10}$ Every 10 years, pop ↑ by 12.6 mil

Table 5.5 U.S. Population (millions) in Census Years Since 1790

$\hat{y} = -2465.6 + 1.36x$

$r^2 = 0.92$

$r = 0.96$

Predictions in L3 and residuals in L4

Year	Pop.	Year	Pop.
1790	3.9	1900	76.2
1800	5.3	1910	92.2
1810	7.2	1920	106.0
1820	9.6	1930	123.2
1830	12.9	1940	132.2
1840	17.1	1950	151.3
1850	23.2	1960	179.3
1860	31.4	1970	203.3
1870	35.6	1980	228.5
1880	50.2	1990	248.8
1890	63.0	2000	281.4
		2010	308.7

Resid vs. xs

A pattern in residuals tells me model is not right

Regression and Correlation: Difficulties and Remedies

Choose quadratic model

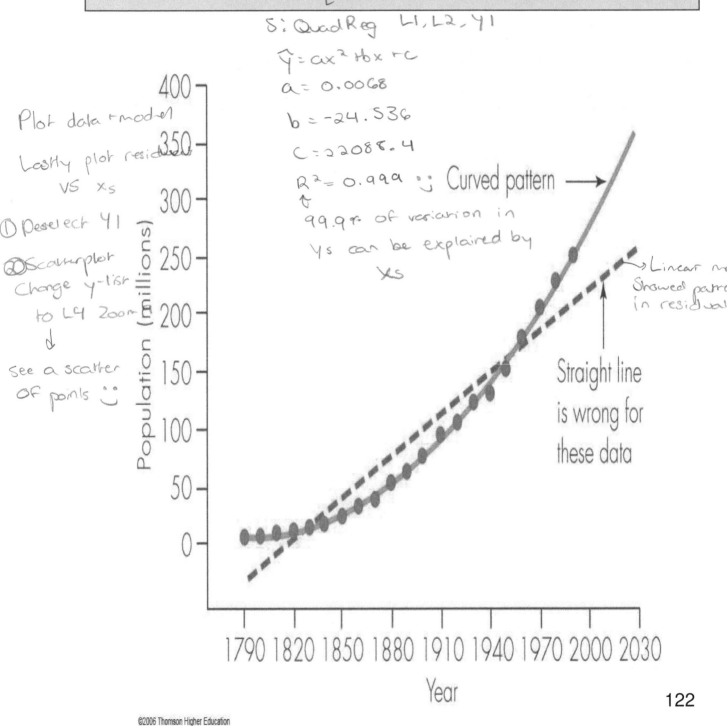

S: QuadReg L1,L2,Y1

$\hat{y} = ax^2 + bx + c$

a = 0.0068

b = -24.536

c = 22088.4

$R^2 = 0.999$ ∴ Curved pattern →

↑

99.9% of variation in Ys can be explained by Xs

Plot data + model

Lastly plot residuals vs Xs

① Deselect Y1

② Scatterplot
Change y-list to L4 Zoom↓

See a scatter of points ☺

→ Linear mod Showed pattern in residuals

Straight line is wrong for these data

Population (millions)

400
350
300
250
200
150
100
50
0

1790 1820 1850 1880 1910 1940 1970 2000 2030

Year

122

Correlation Does Not Prove Causation

$\frac{4}{52} \cdot \frac{48}{51}$

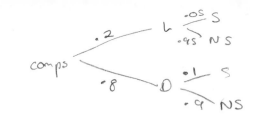

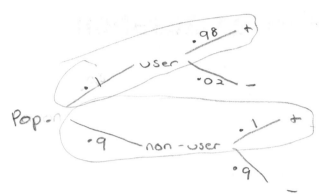

.188

$\frac{.09}{.188}$

$\frac{6}{Die\,1} \cdot \frac{6}{Die\,2} = 36$

Sum 5		Sum 6		Sum 7	
1	4	1	5	1	6
2	3	2	4	2	5
3	2	3	3	3	4
4	1	4	2	4	3
		5	1	5	2
	4		5	6	1
					6

$\frac{15}{36} = .4167$

$\hat{y} = 7.295 - .105x$

1	2	3
O⁺	O⁺	
O⁺		O⁺
	O⁺	O⁺

Chapter 5
Sampling: Surveys and How to Ask Questions

- ## How Data is Collected:
  Observational studies
  randomized experiments

- ## Census → entire population

- ## Sample → a subset of the population

Advantages of a Sample over a Census

- Census Is Not Always Possible

- Speed : time - consuming

- Accuracy : ex. counting homeless as part of the population

- Cost

Fundamental Rule for Using Data for Inference

- Sample data can be used to make inferences about a larger group if the data can be considered to be representative with regard to the question of interest.

Poor example of a sample

  UConn survey: safety on campus

  "Do you feel safe on campus?"

Problem: What does "safe" mean to each person?

Problem: 1274 females ⎤ Big difference here suggests
          410 males   ⎦ a poor sampling plan

A Simple Random Sample

SRS

- Every conceivable group of units of the required size has the same chance of being the selected sample.

Every individual in the population has an equal chance of being selected

Bias: How Surveys Go Wrong

always a problem w/ voluntary response data

- **Selection Bias:** Method for selecting participants that produces a sample that is not representative of the population

  Ex: RateMyProfessor

- **Nonresponse Bias:**
  Individuals are randomly selected to participate, but they cannot answer or they refuse to answer

- **Response Bias:** People do not answer accurately, either intentionally or unintentionally

  Ex: Harvard → incoming freshmen
  "Have you ever cheated on an exam?"

Inference and Margin of Error

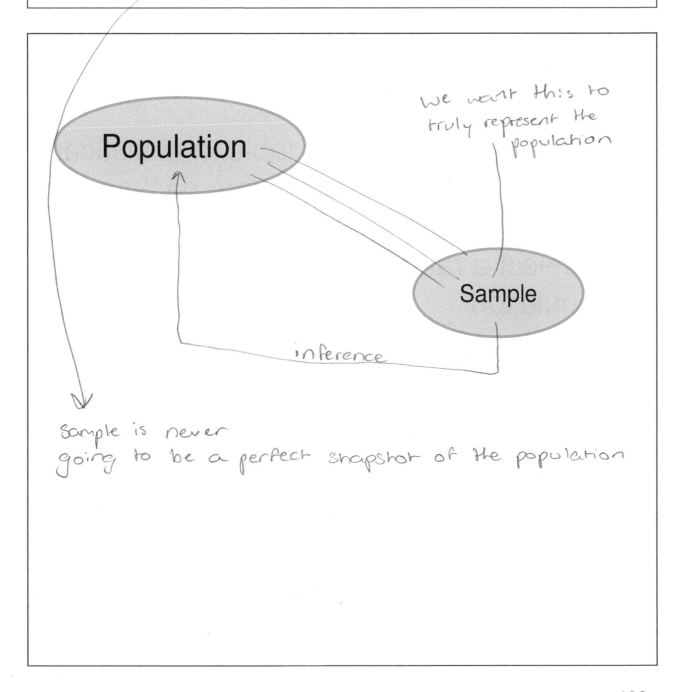

Population

Sample

We want this to truly represent the population

inference

Sample is never going to be a perfect snapshot of the population

Choosing a Simple Random Sample

- Number the units in the population

  Population is UConn students
  ↳ already have Student-Admin #s

- Use a random number table, a statistical calculator, statistical software package or a random number generator on the Web to select a random sample from the population

- **Example:** Suppose you are interested in carrying out a sample survey of students in this class of 256 students.

Choosing a Simple Random Sample
Using the Random Number Table

- . Random Number Table of 2 Digit Numbers:

- *94 90 14 51 40 73 04 33 99*
- *20 79 95 22 36 01 93 10 02*
- *54 85 97 27 27 12 05 72 01*
- *42 30 97 02 83 61 20 98 72*

Choose 5 random numbers 00 to 99

36 01 93 10 02

**Choosing a Simple Random Sample
Using the Random Number Table**

- . Random Number Table of 3 Digit Numbers between 1 and 300:

- *201 182 270 117 250 089 063*
- *125 224 133 054 004 119 134*
- *291 094 101 245 021 126 070*
- *148 243 188 085 223 124 056*

I want 5 students from my class of 256

101 245 021 126 070

Choosing a Simple Random Sample
Using a Graphing Calculator

- · First, on your calculator, set a "seed"

  enter any # into your calculator

  your   [sto →]   math   Prob   select 1: rand
  #
                                    push enter twice

  pick a sample of 5 students
                             beginning end   # of selections
                                # ↓   # ↓   ↓ you want

  Math → prob → 5: randInt (1, 256, 5)
                                      ↓
                                  picking a number slightly
  Pick the 1st 5 non-repeats   higher than 5 prevents
                                      repeats

  or can use 8: randInt No Repeats

A Simple Random Sample

- Sometimes an SRS is not practical

Difficulties in Sampling

- Using the wrong sampling frame

- Not reaching the individuals selected

- Nonresponse or nonparticipation

- Self-selected sample

- Convenience or haphazard sample

Possible sources of response bias in surveys

- Deliberate bias in questions

- Unintentional bias in questions

- Desire of respondents to please

- Asking the uninformed

- Unnecessary Complexity

- Ordering of questions

- Confidentiality and anonymity concerns

Chapter 6
Gathering Useful Data for Examining Relationships

- How are variables related?

- If we change one variable, will it cause a change in another variable?

Two Basic Types of Statistical Research Studies

- Observational studies

- Randomized Experiments

Explanatory and Response Variables

- •Explanatory Variables:

- •Response Variables:

Confounding and Lurking Variables

•Confounding Variables:

•Lurking Variables:

For each of the examples, decide whether the study was an observational study or a randomized experiment

1. A group of 100 students was randomly divided with 50 assigned to receive vitamin C and the remaining 50 to receive a placebo, to determine whether vitamin C helps to prevent colds.

2. All patients who received a hip transplant operation at Stanford University Hospital during 1995-2005 will be followed for ten years after their operation to determine the success (or failure) of the transplant.

3.   A group of students who were enrolled in an introductory statistics course were randomly assigned to take a Web-based course or a traditional lecture course. The two methods were compared by giving the same final exam in both courses.

4.   A group of smokers and a group of nonsmokers who visited a particular clinic were asked to come in for a physical exam every five years for the rest of their lives so that the researchers could monitor and compare their health status.

Designing a Good Experiment

•Randomization

Case Study 6.2: Kids and Weight Lifting

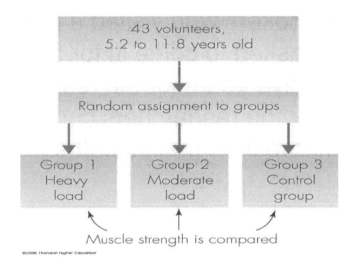

Choosing a Random Sample

- **Case Study 6.2:** Suppose we want to randomly assign 15 children to Group 1, 16 children to Group 2 and 12 children to the Control group..

1. Label the children from 01 to 43

2. Use TI Calculator to do the randomization.

Group1:

Group 2:

Control:

- Control Group:

- Placebo Group:

- Blinding:

    Double blind:

    Single blind:

Observational Study

- Disadvantage:

- Advantage:

- ## Case-Control Studies:

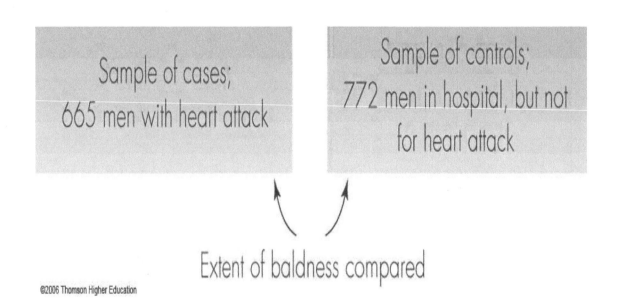

Sample of cases;
665 men with heart attack

Sample of controls;
772 men in hospital, but not
for heart attack

Extent of baldness compared

Experiments and Observational Studies

- Probably the biggest misinterpretation made when reporting studies is to imply that a cause-and-effect relationship can be concluded on the basis of an observational study.

The Rule for Concluding Cause and Effect: "cause-and-effect" relationships may be inferred from randomized experiments but not from observational studies.

Chapter 7
Probability

we use sample data to generalize to a population

- ## Probability and Statistical Inference

  When we use sample information to make conclusions about a population we rely on **probability**

  ‖
  ∨

  Talking about random fluctuations among samples from a population

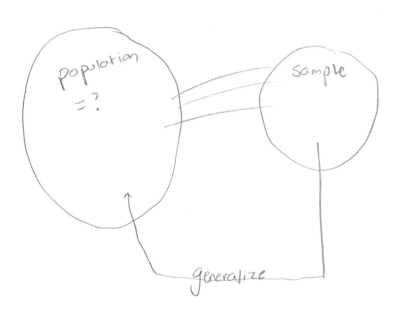

Population =?

Sample

generalize

Problem: samples vary →
By how much do they vary? → need probability

Probability

- ## The way we quantify uncertainty

Roll a die. Will I roll a 3? → unknown → it's
    a random event

What are the chances of rolling a 3?
        likelihood

$= \dfrac{1}{6}$ → 1 way of rolling a 3

↳ 6 possible outcomes
(We know the outcomes
  are equally likely
↳ We call this our sample space for random event

$S = \{1, 2, 3, 4, 5, 6\}$

Prob of 3 = $P(3) = \dfrac{1}{6}$ → it's the long range
    likelihood of an outcome

The Effect of Aspirin on Heart Attacks

Randomized experiment → prove cause + effect

sample data {

	Heart Attacks	Drs. In Group	Attacks per 1000 Drs.
Aspirin	104	11,037	9.4
Placebo	189	11,034	17.1

Aspirin: $\frac{104}{11037} = \frac{0.0094}{1} = \frac{9.4}{1000}$

Placebo:

We want to generalize from the sample to the population

Is the difference (9.4 vs. 17.1) a "real" difference (statistically significant)?

Or is it simply random fluctuation among samples?

To answer this, we need probability

Probability and Random Events

① Random events → whenever we have a situation where the individual outcomes cannot be determined, but a pattern develops in the long run

    Ex. Flip a coin

    Ex. insurance companies use actuarial tables

② Probability of an outcome of a random event is the likelihood the outcome will occur in the long run

    Two approaches:
      ① Theoretical probability → based on known characteristics of a random event
        Ex. Dice, cards, lotteries, casino games

      ② Relative frequency probability → we need to collect a large amount of data

        Ex. insurance companies → car insurance

163

Theoretical Probability *and*
Relative Frequency Interpretation of Probability

Roll a die $P(3) =$

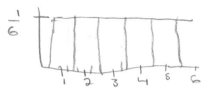

A. Theoretical prob.
   ① Sample space $\{1, 2, 3, 4, 5, 6\}$

   ② Outcomes equally likely? yes

B. Relative freq. probability — Data!
   ① Roll a die 20 times

   not enough rolls to get a
   good indication of $P(3)$

   ② Roll die 500 times

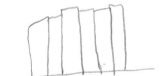

Math → PROB
5: rand Int (1, 6, 20)
   Sto → L1 enter

2nd Y= ▱▱▱ L1
                  1

Zoom 9

Window   xmin: 1   Graph
          xmax: 7
          xscale: 1

Relative Frequency Interpretation of Probability

- The probability of a specific outcome is the proportion of times the outcome would occur **over the long run**

- **Example:**

  According to the U.S. Center for Disease Control, the long-run relative frequency of males born in the United States is nearly 0.512

  $P(m) = 0.512 \rightarrow$
  This is a good estimate of the underlying probability of being born male

Relative Frequency Interpretation of Probability

- The probability of a specific outcome is the proportion of times the outcome would occur **over the long run**

Table 7.1 Relative Frequency of Male Births over Time _— in one hospital_

Weeks of Watching	Total Births	Total Boys	Proportion of Boys	
1	30	19	.633	$\frac{19}{30}$
4	116	68	.586	$\frac{68}{116}$
13	317	172	.543	
26	623	383	.615	
39	919	483	.526	
52	1237	639	.517	

©2006 Thomson Higher Education

Relative Frequency Interpretation of Probability

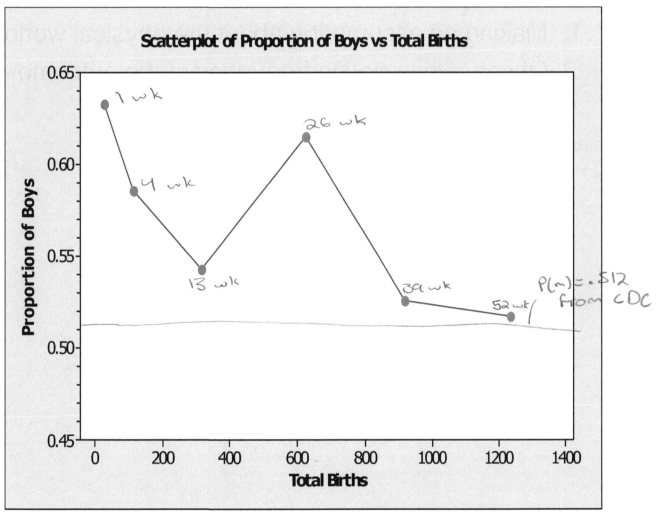

Scatterplot of Proportion of Boys vs Total Births

Random Fluctuation → as the amount of data ↑, the relative freq. prob. will eventually settle down to ≈ theoretical prob.

Theoretical Probability and Relative Frequency Probability

- theoretical

  Two ways to determine probability:

  1. Making an assumption about the physical world

  2. Observe the relative frequency of the outcome over many, many repetitions of the situation

- **Example 1:**

CT Daily Numbers

 Pick 3 digits $\{0,1,2,\ldots 9\}$

  Buy 1 ticket $P(w) = ?$

Theoretical approach

 1. Sample space $\{000, 001, 002, \ldots 999\}$
 2. Are outcomes equally likely? Yes

   $P(w) = \frac{1}{1000}$

Relative freq approach: collect a large amount of data

  Buy 100s of tickets

  $P(w) \approx \dfrac{\text{# of winning tickets}}{\text{total # of tickets}}$

Theoretical Probability and Relative Frequency Probability

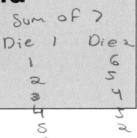

Sum of 7

Die 1	Die 2
1	6
2	5
3	4
4	3
5	2
6	1

- Two ways to determine a probability:

  1. Making an assumption about the physical world

  2. Observe the relative frequency of the outcome over many, many repetitions of the situation

- **Example 2:** Roll 2 dice

  $$P(\text{sum of } 7) = \frac{6}{36} = .167$$

  Theoretical:

  Sample space $\{2, 3, 4, \ldots 12\}$

  Are these outcomes equally likely? No!

  Can I figure out all the unique possible outcomes?

  Use Fundamental Principle of Counting:

  Subdivide the event into its individual components

  # of outcomes $\left(\underbrace{\frac{6}{\text{Die 1}} \times \frac{6}{\text{Die 2}}}_{\text{equally likely}} = 36 \text{ equally likely outcomes}\right)$

169

Theoretical Probability and Relative Frequency Probability

- Two ways to determine a probability:
  1. Making an assumption about the physical world
  → 2. Observe the relative frequency of the outcome over many, many repetitions of the situation

- **Example 2:**

Collect data or simulate data

Roll 1 die 250 times and store it in L1

Roll 2nd die 250 times and store it in L2

Stat → edit → highlight L3 enter $P(7) \approx \frac{n}{250}$

L3 = L1 + L2

Create a histogram of L3

xlist: L3   Window   xmin = 2

Freq: 1   xmax = 13   Graph

                                  xscale = 1

Trace

min = 2

max 08   n = ?

Blood types $\{A, B, AB, O\}$

I select 1 person - can I say p(person has Type B) $= \frac{1}{4}$?
No; can't assume blood types are equally likely

Relative Frequency Interpretation of Probability vs. Theoretical Probability

- Two ways to determine probability:

  1. Making an assumption about the physical world

  2. Collecting Data

- **Example 3:**

Toss a coin

Theo prob:

$$S = \{H, T\}$$

Outcomes equally likely? Yes

$$P(H) = \frac{1}{2} \quad P(T) = \frac{1}{2}$$

Rel freq prob

$$P(H) \approx \frac{\# \text{ of times heads appears}}{\text{total} \# \text{ of flips}}$$

the larger the better

Toss a thumbtack

$$S = \{\perp, \Gamma\}$$

Outcomes equally likely?
Unknown

Can't calc theo prob

Only way to find prob of way it lands is to collect lots of data

Minitab Ch4: Using Simulation to Find Probabilities

Minitab Ch4: Using Simulation to Find Probabilities

Probability: Conditions and Definitions

- Sample Space: All possible outcomes

Roll a die $S = \{1, 2, 3, 4, 5, 6\}$ equally likely

Flip 2 coins $S = \{2\ heads,\ H+T,\ 2\ tails\}$ not equally likely

$S = \{HH, HT, TH, TT\}$

- Simple Event:

Probability: Conditions and Definitions

- ## Conditions:

② $\sum P \binom{all\ simple}{events} = 1$

① $0 \leq P(A) \leq 1$
$\downarrow$
a particular outcome or
combination of outcomes

- ## Equally likely events:

Make sure if you use this idea, it is valid

Coin: H or T → = likely

Blood types → not = likely

Ex 7.41: Prizes in Cereal Boxes

A, B, C, D, E

- A particular brand of cereal contains a prize in each box. There are five possible prizes, and any box is equally likely to contain each of the 5 prizes. Suppose you purchase 2 boxes of cereal. What is the probability that you will receive the same prize in each box? What is the probability that you will receive two different prizes?

Sample Space = $\left\{ \begin{array}{cc} \text{Prize in} & \text{Prize in} \\ \text{Box 1} & \text{Box 2} \end{array} \right\}$

How many different possibilities?

Fundamental Principle of Counting

$$\frac{5}{\text{Box 1}} \times \frac{5}{\text{Box 2}} = 25 \text{ equally likely events}$$

$$P(\text{any simple outcome}) = \frac{1}{25}$$

Same prize: AA, BB, CC, DD, EE $= \frac{5}{25}$

$$P(2 \text{ diff. prizes}) = 1 - \frac{5}{25} = \frac{20}{25}$$

Basic Rules for
Finding Probabilities

- Complementary Events:

  Event A   complement of A: not A, A^c, $\bar{A}$

  venn Diagram

- Rule: $P(A) + P(A^c) = 1$

- **Example:** A recent poll from the Conn. Center for Survey Research stated that 45% of those polled felt that it was

  rel. freq.

  possible for individuals to do something about global warming.

  A: Do something about global warming

  $P(A) \approx .45$

Basic Rules for Finding Probabilities

- ## Mutually Exclusive Events: events that cannot occur together

Event A: getting an A on a test 1

   P(A on test 1) = .55

Event B: getting a B or C on test 1

   P(B or C on T1) = .35

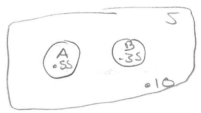

Rule:

Addition Rule for Mutually Exclusive Events

P(A or B) = P(A) + P(B) = .55 + .35 = .90

Basic Rules for Finding Probabilities

- Ex: What is the probability that a woman who has two children has either two girls or two boys?

A: 2 girls

B: 2 boys

Outcomes mutually exclusive? yes

Are events = likely? Yes

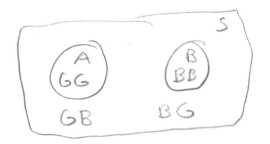

Rule#2b:

$$P(A \text{ or } B) = P(A) + P(B)$$

$$\frac{1}{4} + \frac{1}{4} = \frac{1}{2}$$

Basic Rules for Finding Probabilities

- Events that are **not** mutually exclusive:

A: person is a smoker

B: person has lung cancer

Are these mutually exclusive? No

4 regions

Region 1: A and B^C

Region 2: A and B

Region 3: A^C and B

Region 4: A^C and B^C

Rule:

$$P(A \text{ or } B) = \underbrace{P(A)}_{\substack{\text{Regions} \\ 1+2}} + \underbrace{P(B)}_{\substack{\text{Regions} \\ 2+3}} - \underbrace{P(A \text{ and } B)}_{\text{Region 2}}$$

180

Basic Rules for Finding Probabilities

- ## Ex:

Medical rehab facility
for veterans
                2000 veterans

A: PTSD 580

B: Physical injuries 620

A and B: 430

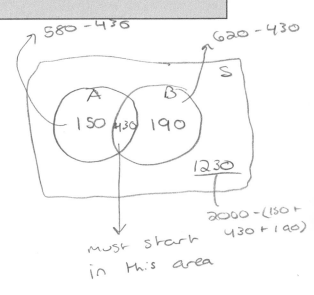

580 - 430

620 - 430

150 430 190

1230

must start
in this area

2000 - (150 +
430 + 190)

Rule:

Suppose I select 1 person

$$P(A \text{ or } B) = \frac{150 + 430 + 190}{2000} = 0.385$$

$$P(A^c \text{ or } B^c) = \frac{190 + 1230 + 150}{2000} = 0.785$$

$$P(A^c \text{ or } B) = \frac{190 + 1230 + 430}{2000} = 0.925$$

181

- **Example:** An individual is considering laser eye surgery to correct her vision. The eye surgeon explains the risks to the patient. Infection occurs in 1.5% of such operations, the surgery is not a complete success and must be redone in 6%, and both infection and the need to be redone occur together in 0.5% of the surgeries. (Use a diagram to represent this situation.) What is the probability that the operation succeeds and is free from infection?

$\sim .015$

$I :$ infection $= .015$

$R :$ redone $= .06$

I and $B = .005$

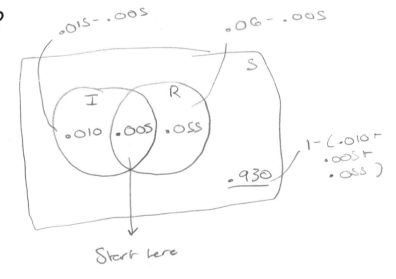

.015 - .005   .06 - .005

$1 - (.010 +$
$.005 +$
$.055)$

Start here

or means one
or the other or
both

① $P(I$ and $R) = .005$

② $P(I$ or $R) = .010 + .005 + .055$

③ $P(I^C$ and $R^C) = .930$

Basic Rules for Finding Probabilities

- Conditional Probability: → looking @ a subset
  of the entire sample space

P(A occurs given that B has occurred)

P(A|B)

For example:

P(Heart disease | high cholesterol)

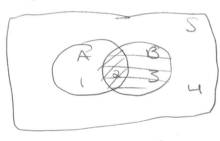

4 regions

$P(A|B) = \dfrac{Region\ 2}{Regions\ 2\ and\ 3}$

↓
focusing on this area

Basic Rules for Finding Probabilities

- **Example (cont.):** Given that the surgery must be redone, what is the probability that an infection occurred?

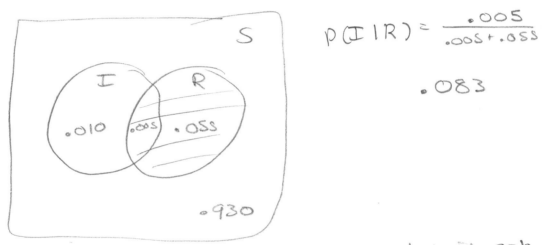

$$P(I \mid R) = \frac{.005}{.005 + .055}$$

$$.083$$

Suppose an infection occurred, what is prob. the surgery needs to be redone?

$$P(R \mid I) = \frac{.005}{.010 + .005} = .333$$

$$P(R^c \mid I) = \frac{.010}{.010 + .005} = .667$$

SUM = 1

Probability Examples

- **Example:** If there are 2500 incoming first-year students at UConn and 24% of them enroll in Stat 1100, 16% enroll in Math 1130 and 5% enroll in both Stat 1110 and Math 1131.

- Define the following events:
    - A: Student is enrolled in Stat 1100
    - B: Student is enrolled in Math 1131

- Use a diagram to represent this information

185

Probability Examples

- **Example (cont.):**

If we randomly select one student, find the following probabilities:

1. P(A or B)

2. P(A^C)

3. P(B^C)

4. P(A and B)

5. P(A|B)

6. P(B|A)

Basic Rules for Finding Probabilities

- ## Independent Events: one event has no effect on another event

Ex. Flip 2 coins   A: Heads on 1st coin

                           B: Heads on 2nd coin

Ex. Flip 10 coins   A: Heads on 1st 9 flips

                           B: Heads on 10th

- ## Rule:

P(A and B) if A and B are independent =

$$P(A) \times P(B)$$

$$\frac{1}{2} \cdot \frac{1}{2} = \frac{1}{4}$$

Basic Rules for
Finding Probabilities

- ## Dependent Events: 2 events that are related to one another

Ex. Lung cancer and smoking

A   B

- ## Rule:

$$P(A \text{ and } B) = P(A) \cdot P(B|A)$$

Calculating Probabilities When Sampling With Replacement

- **Example:** Draw 3 cards with replacement from a shuffled deck of 52 cards. What is the probability that you select 3 Aces?

$P(A_1 \text{ and } A_2 \text{ and } A_3)$

If I sample w/ replacement then I know selections are independent

$\rightarrow P(A_1) \cdot P(A_2) \cdot P(A_3)$

$\frac{4}{52} \cdot \frac{4}{52} \cdot \frac{4}{52} = \left(\frac{4}{52}\right)^3 = .000455$

Calculating Probabilities When Sampling Without Replacement

- **Example:** Draw 3 cards <u>without</u> replacement from a shuffled deck of 52 cards. What is the probability that you select 3 Aces?

When selecting w/o replacement, selections are now dependent

$P(A_1 \text{ and } A_2 \text{ and } A_3) =$

$P(A_1) \cdot P(A_2 | A_1) \cdot P(A_3 | A_1 \text{ and } A_2)$

$\frac{4}{52} \cdot \frac{3}{51} \cdot \frac{2}{50} = 1.8099...\ E-4$

$.00018099$

Calculating Probabilities When Sampling Without Replacement from Large Populations

- If a small sample is drawn from a large population, the distinction between sampling with and without replacement becomes less visible.

  There is very little difference between 2 results

  The sample should be < 5% of the population

- **Example:** Casinos use several decks of cards at Blackjack tables (to avoid card-counting). Suppose at one particular casino, a "shoe" with 7 decks is used. If 3 cards are drawn from the deck (without replacement), what is the probability that all 3 cards are Aces?

  → dependent events

  $7 \cdot 52 = 364$ cards

  $7 \cdot 4 = 28$ aces

  $P(A_1 \text{ and } A_2 \text{ and } A_3)$

  $\frac{28}{364} \cdot \frac{27}{363} \cdot \frac{26}{362} = .09041$ — very close

  w/ replacement:

  $\frac{28}{364} \cdot \frac{28}{364} \cdot \frac{28}{364} = \left(\frac{28}{364}\right)^3 = .00045$

191

Calculating Probabilities When Sampling Without Replacement from Large Populations

Ex. Suppose I know that ≈ 8% of all UConn students smoke

But I don't know exact population size ≈ 20,000

Suppose I select 1 student randomly

$$P(\text{smoker}) = .08 \qquad P(\text{smoker}^c) = .92$$
$$\underset{\text{not smoker}}{\uparrow}$$

Suppose I select 10 students randomly w/o replacement

$$\underset{\text{selections are dependent}}{\underbrace{}}$$

I can then treat the problem as if the selections of the population are independent → Because my population is large + sample is small

P(all 10 students are non-smokers)

$$P(S_1^c \text{ and } S_2^c \ldots S_{10}^c)$$
$$\downarrow$$
$$(.92)(.92) \ldots (.92)$$

$$(.92)^{10} \approx .43 \text{ or } 43\%$$

P(at least one student smokes)

$$1 - .43 = .57$$

Tree Diagrams

- A Tree diagram is a useful way of displaying information in steps:

  ① Repetitive process

  ② 2 step process

Tree Diagram

- The manufacturer of a smoke alarm advertises that the alarm they manufacture will operate properly 95% of the time. If a home is equipped with three of these alarms, what is the probability that at least one functions properly at any given time? Assume that the alarms operate independently.

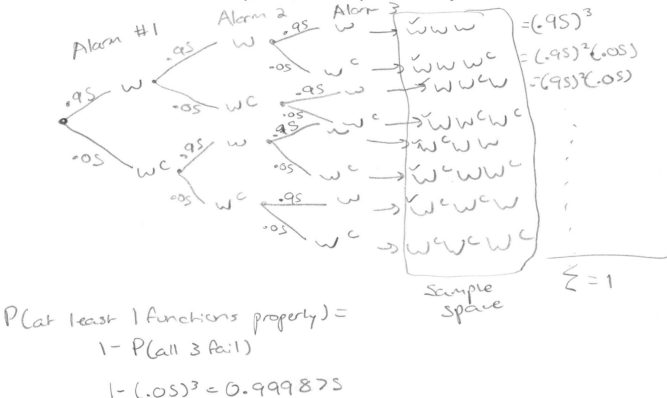

$$P(\text{at least 1 functions properly}) =$$
$$1 - P(\text{all 3 fail})$$
$$1 - (.05)^3 = 0.999875$$

Tree Diagram

Seemingly large populations for diseases that are rare can result in significant incorrect results

- **Example:** Tests that are designed to detect cancer must be very accurate. However, there is always a small risk of a 'false positive' or 'false negative' result. In the case of breast cancer detection, a mammogram is the most commonly used test. The chances of a false positive test are reported to be 0.05. The chances of a false negative are reported to be 0.025. It is also known that approximately 10% of women will develop breast cancer in their lifetimes. Suppose a woman has a mammogram and gets a positive result, what are the chances that she actually has breast cancer?

$$P(BrCa \mid +) = \frac{.10(.975)}{.10(.975) + .90(.05)} = .684 \quad 68.4\%$$

$$P(BrCa^c \mid +) = \frac{.90(.05)}{.10(.975) + .90(.05)} = .316 \quad 31.6\%$$

$$> = 1$$

195

Probability Examples

- **Example:** The FAA studies the number of flights that arrive on time. The following refers to data on flights leaving from O'Hare airport in Chicago and traveling to major coastal cities.

  A: (Chicago to NY flight is on time)

  B: (Chicago to Atlanta flight is on time)

  C: (Chicago to Los Angeles flight is on time)

  $P(A) = 0.6$

  $P(B) = 0.7$

  $P(C) = 0.8$

  Suppose on any given day, there is one flight to each of these cities on one of the major carriers. Represent these events with a tree diagram.

Probability Examples

- **Example (cont.):** Tree Diagram

Probability Examples

- **Example (cont.):** Use the tree diagram to calculate the following probabilities:

1. P(all 3 flights are on time):

2. P(at least one flight is <u>not</u> on time)

3. P(only the New York flight is on time)

4. P(exactly one of the three flights is on time)

Using Simulation to Estimate Probabilities

Chapter 8: Random Variables

Count data and measurement data

↓   ↓

discrete models   continuous models

↓   ↓

        binomial models   → normal model
            or
      geometric model   → uniform
           or

       Poissom model

- **Random Event:** not haphazard

  An individual outcome is not predictable

  Patterns develop over the long run

  $$P(\text{heads over long run}) = \tfrac{1}{2}$$

- **Random Variable:** A variable (x)

  that assigns a numerical value to
  each outcome of a random event

  Define x : # on face of a die $S = \{1, 2, 3, 4, 5, 6\}$

  Ex : Interview 2 people. Do you smoke?

  $$S = \{ \overset{2}{SS}, \overset{1}{SS^c}, \overset{1}{S^cS}, \overset{0}{S^cS^c} \}$$

  Define x : # of smokers

Classes of Random Variables

1.   A discrete random variable can take one of a **countable** list of distinct values.

Ex.

X: # of ppl w/ O$^+$ blood in a group of 10 ppl

List of possible values of x:

$\{0, 1, 2, 3, \ldots, 10\}$

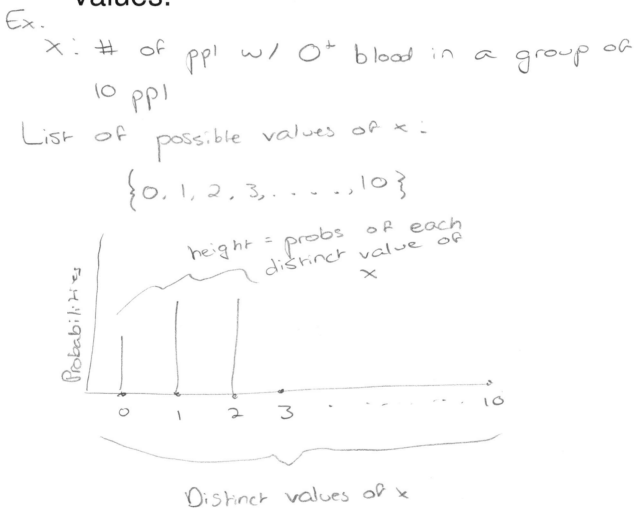

Distinct values of x

Classes of Random Variables

1.   A <u>continuous random</u> variable can take any <u>value in an interval or collection of intervals.</u>

X : measurement data

Ex: x is height of adult women

Shortest   Tallest

↓

Probability sits anywhere
along this interval

206

count data

Discrete Random Variables

Notation: X → define what I am counting

k → possible values of x

$\boxed{P(X = k)}$

probability statement

•**Example:** Suppose we want to know the probability that, of the next three births in a hospital, two will be girls.

X : # of girls

k-values : 0, 1, 2, or 3

$P(x = 2)$ or $P(2)$

The probability distribution function (pdf) for a discrete random variable _X_ is a table or rule that assigns probabilities to the possible values of the random variable _X._

- **Example:** Toss a coin twice

$$S = \{HH, HT, TH, TT\}$$

Define x: # of heads

Can I construct a pdf? Yes

  IF I know something about the characteristics
  of this random event

  If coin is fair → all outcomes are
    equally likely

x	$P(x=k)$
0	1/4
1	1/2
2	1/4

k-values

→ called a pdf

- **Example 8.5:** Suppose 35% of the students at a college take 4 courses, 45% take 5 courses, and 20% take 6 courses.

relative freqs

x: # of courses

k: 4, 5, 6

possible k-values

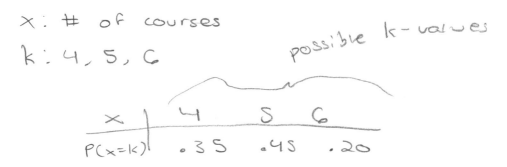

x	4	5	6
$P(x=k)$	.35	.45	.20

- Conditions for Probabilities for Discrete Random Variables:

$$0 \le P(x=k) \le 1$$

and

$$\sum P(x=k) = 1$$

Probability Distribution for the Number of Girls in a Family of 3 Children

$x = $ # of girls   possible values: $0, 1, 2, 3$

pdf

X	$P(x=k)$
0	1/8
1	3/8
2	3/8
3	1/8

Theoretical prob.

① How many outcomes?

$$\frac{2}{\#1} \times \frac{2}{\#2} \times \frac{2}{\#3} = 8$$

② Are these outcomes equally likely?

Yes if we assume $P(B) = P(G) = 1/2$

X	$P(x=k)$
0	$.512^3$
1	$3(.488)(.512)^2$
2	$3(.488)^2(.512)$
3	$.488^3$

relative freq. prob. → comes from actual data

CDC tells us

$P(B) = .512$

$P(G) = .488$

Graphing the Probability Distribution

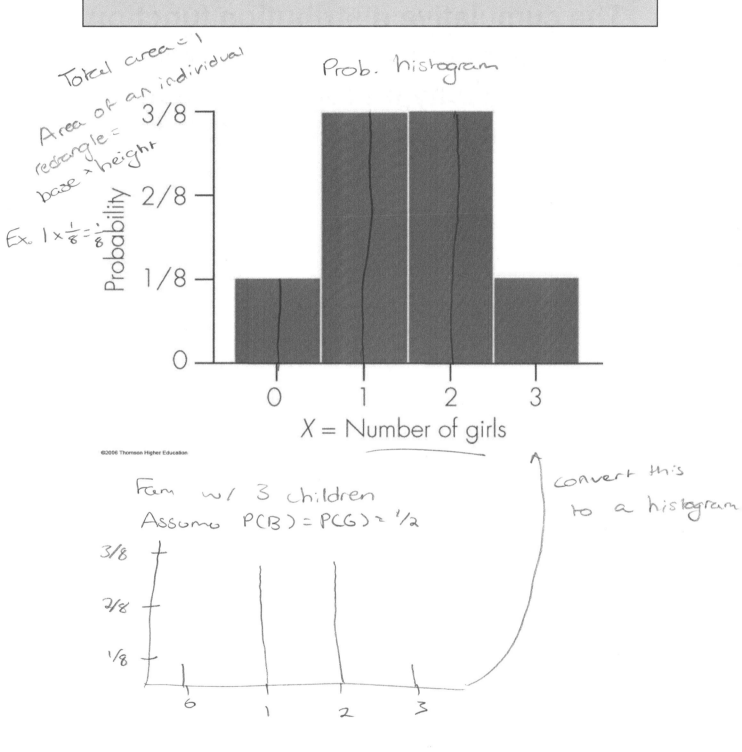

Total area = 1

Area of an individual rectangle = base × height

Ex. $1 \times \frac{1}{8} = \frac{1}{8}$

Prob. histogram

3/8

2/8

Probability

1/8

0

0   1   2   3

$X =$ Number of girls

©2006 Thomson Higher Education

Fam w/ 3 children
Assume $P(B) = P(G) = \frac{1}{2}$

3/8
2/8
1/8

0   1   2   3

convert this to a histogram

211

> **The <u>cumulative distribution function</u> (cdf)** for a random variable *X* provides the probability that *X* is less than or equal to a particular value *k*, $P(X \leq k)$.

x = # of girls in fam of 3

$$P(B) = P(G) = 1/2$$

pdf

→ k-values

x	0	1	2	3
$P(x=k)$	1/8	3/8	3/8	1/8

cdf

x	0	1	2	3
$P(x \leq k)$	1/8	4/8	7/8	1

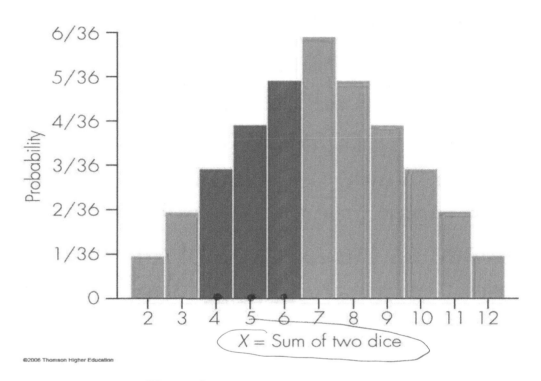

Graph of the Probability Distribution for the Sum of Two dice

©2006 Thomson Higher Education

$P(\overset{\longleftrightarrow}{4 \leq X \leq 6})$ or $P(x = 4, 5, \text{ or } 6)$

$\dfrac{3}{36} + \dfrac{4}{36} + \dfrac{5}{36} = \dfrac{12}{36}$

→ this is the same statement

$P(3 < x < 7)$ Starts @ 4 and ends @ 6

$P(x \leq 4)$ or $P(x < 5)$ → means $x = 2, 3, 4$

$\underbrace{\qquad\qquad}_{6/36}$

complement

$P(x > 4)$ or $P(x \geq 5) = \dfrac{30}{36}$

213

The **expected value** of a random variable X is the mean value of the variable in the sample space or population of possible outcomes. Expected value can also be interpreted as the mean value that would be obtained as the average of an infinite number of observations of the random variable.

Mean = E(X) = μ = $\Sigma(x_i \cdot p_i)$

individual x-values

of a random variable x

individual probabilities

- **Example:** Suppose you work for an insurance company, and you sell a $10,000 one-year term insurance policy at an annual premium of $290. The chance that the client dies during the year is (0.001.) What is the expected gain for the company?

comes from data

Outcome	Gain, X	Probability
Customer lives	290	0.999
Customer dies	290 − 10,000	0.001

x: $ the company makes on a policy over the long run

Expected gain = $E(x)$ = mean = μ

Stat → edit → clear L1 and L2

L1	L2
290	.999
290-10000	.001

Interpretation:

Stat → calc → 1-var stats → xlist L1 freqlist L2 $280

In the long run, the company gains, on average, $280 per policy

215

Standard Deviation for a Discrete Random Variable

The standard deviation of a discrete random variable quantifies how spread out the possible values of a discrete random variable might be, weighted by how likely each value is to occur.

Formula:

$$\sigma = \sqrt{\sum(x_i - \mu)^2 \, p_i}$$

Note: $p_i = P(X = x_i)$

On the TI 83/84: on calc, σx

Ex. 8.13: Same Mean, Different Standard Deviation

- Suppose you decide to invest $~~$100~~ 500 in a scheme that you hope will make some money. You have two choices of investment plans and you must choose one. The possible net gains 1 year later and their probabilities are:

x: net gain

Choice 1

L1	L2
x	$P(x=k)$
5000	.001
1000	.005
0	.994

Choice 2

x	$P(x=k)$
20	.30
10	.20
4	.80

$\bar{x}$ = Expected gain = $\boxed{\$10}$ $\longrightarrow$ $\mu = \boxed{\$10}$

$\sigma x = \$173$ $\sigma x = \$7$

more variable/volatile than Choice 2

Specific type of discrete random variable

A **binomial random variable** is defined as X = number of successes in n trials of a binomial experiment

A **binomial experiment** is defined by the following conditions:

How many people are we polling

1. There are n "trials," where n is specified in advance and is not a random value.

2. There are two possible outcomes on each trial, called "success" or "failure."

3. The outcomes are independent from one trial to the next.

4. The probability of a "success" remains the same from one trial to the next, and this probability is denoted by p. The probability of a "failure" is $1-p$ for every trial.

- **Example:** For each of the following random circumstances determine if it is a binomial experiment or not. If it is a binomial experiment find the values of *n* and *p.*

1. Toss three fair coins: X = number of heads.

    1. $n = 3$
    2. 2 outcomes, H or T
    3. Tosses are ind.
    4. P(H) is always equal to 1/2

    Binomial

2. A fair die is rolled 30 times: X = number of times a 2 is rolled.

    1. $n = 30$
    2. outcomes "2" or "not 2"
    3. Ind.
    4. P(2) = 1/6   p(not 2) = 5/6

    Binomal

3. A football team plays 12 games in its regular season: X = number of games the team wins.

    1. $n = 12$
    2. outcomes W or L
    3. Outcomes ind → maybe yes or maybe no
    4. P(win) → changes depending on quality of opponent

    Not binomial

4. A poker hand consists of 5 cards *Drawn w/o replacement* drawn from a deck of 52 cards:

X = the number of aces in a hand.

1. $n = 5$
2. outcomes Ace or not ace
3. Are selections ind.? No b/c w/o replacement
4. P(A) changes after each selection

Not binomial

5. Randomly sample 1000 U.S. adults:

X = number who have seen a UFO. *from U.S. pop*

1. $n = 1000$
2. Outcomes yes or no
3. Are selections ind.? Technically no, but because we're selecting w/o replacement, we can say they are ≈ ind b/c pop is so large and sample is so small
4. P(yes) → stays ≈ throughout the expriment

≈ binomial

- **Example 8.15:** Suppose the probability that you win a game is 0.2 for each play and the plays of the game are independent of one another.

Let X = number of wins in three plays.

$n = 3$

Binomial Outcomes W or L

game outcomes are ind.

$P(\cup) = 0.2$

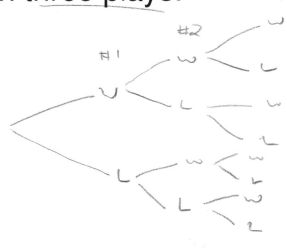

pdf

So the probability distribution of X is:

X	$P(x=k)$	
0	$(0.8)^3$	→ LLL
k-values 1	$3(0.2)(.8)^2$	→ WLL, LWL, LLW
2	$3(.2)^2(.8)$	→ WWL, WLW, LWW
3	$(0.2)^3$	→ WWW

→ huge tree w/ many branches

- Let's suppose n=10. What is P(X=2)?

$$P(x=2) \quad \underline{\qquad} (.2)^2 (.8)^8$$

↓
??

# of paths that result in 2 W and 8 L

- Where did the <u>numerical coefficients</u> come from? /

Use the combination formula

on calc

nCr "n choose r"

10 → math → prob → nCr → 2 ⟶ "10 choose 2"

$= 45$

- Binomial Formula:

$$P(x=k) = nC_k \, (p)^k (1-p)^{n-k}$$

↓   ↓

specific value   really r
                  on calc

- Use the Binomial formula to calculate P(X= 2) for the previous problem.

$$P(x=2) = nC_2 (.2)^2 (.8)^8 = 0.302$$

- **Example:** This is the graph of the probability distribution for X = number of wins in 3 plays.

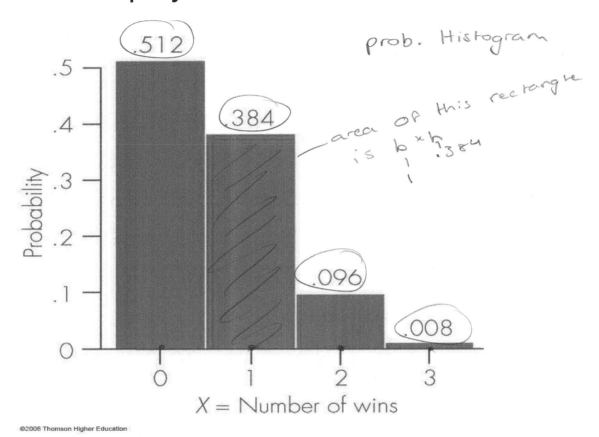

prob. Histogram

area of this rectangle is b × h .384

©2006 Thomson Higher Education

Use the Binomial Formula to verify that $P(X=1) = 0.384$

Area of rectangle at x=1

$3C_1 (.2)^1 (.8)^2$

Calculating Binomial Probabilities on the TI-83/84

1. Press 2nd, VARS to reach the **Distribution** menu.

2. To find P($X=k$), the proabability of exactly k successes, use **A:binompdf(**. Enter numerical values for n, p, k (separated by commas) and enter the closing parenthesis.

3. To find P$(X \leq k)$, the cumulative probability of k or fewer successes, use **B:binomcdf(**. Enter the numerical values for n, p, k (separated by commas) and enter the closing parenthesis.

Calculating Binomial probabilities on the TI-83/84

x= whatever we define as success

Ex: n = 6   p(success) = .52

pdf

X	P(x= k)
0	.0122
1	.0795
2	.2103
3	.3110
4	.2827
5	.1095
6	.0198

cdf

X	P(x≤k)
0	.0122
1	.0917
2	.3070
3	.6180
4	.8707
5	.9082
6	1

A: binomialpdf
   trials: 6
      p: .52
   x value : 0

B:

Example 8.17: You have been busy lately, so busy that you're surprised to learn when you arrive at today's statistics class that a 15-questions true-false quiz is on the agenda. The quiz is about readings you haven't done, so you are forced to guess at every question.

$X =$ correct answers

$n = 15$ $\qquad p = p(\text{correct}) = \frac{1}{2}$

1. What is the probability that you will get exactly 7 questions correct? $P(x=7) = 0.1964$
   $\downarrow$
   binomial pdf

2. What is the probability that you will get at most 7 questions correct? $P(x \le 7) = .500$
   $\downarrow$
   cdf

3. You will pass the test if you get 10 or more correct answers. What is the probability that you pass the test? $P(x \ge 10) \rightarrow$ calculate complement and subtract from 1

Binom cdf: $x \le$ ___

$P(x \le 9)$

$1 - " = .1509$

4. What is the probability that you will get 5 to 10 questions correct?

Bincdf (15. 5,10) — Binomcdf (15, .5, 4)

. 8815

Ex. A pharmaceutical company claims that 20% of those taking its new allergy medication will experience drowsiness. To test this claim it randomly assigns 500 people to take the new medication.

$X =$ # who experience drowsiness

$n = 500$ $p = .20$

x	$P(x=k)$
0	small numbers
1	
2	
:	
:	
:	
500	

1. What is the probability that exactly 100 of those people will experience drowsiness? $P(x=100)$

   pdf

   .0446

2. What is the probability that at least 100 of those people will experience drowsiness? $P(x \geq 100)$

   cdf $\rightarrow$ complement

   $1 - P(x \leq 99)$

3. What is the probability that between 75 and 120 (inclusive) of those people will experience drowsiness?

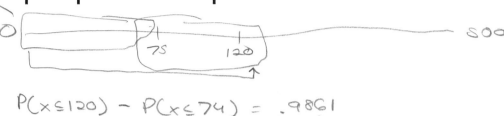

Subtract

$P(x \leq 120) - P(x \leq 74) = .9861$

4. What is the probability that at most 110 of those people will experience drowsiness?

$P(x \leq 110) = .8790$

5. What is the probability that fewer than 110 of those people will experience drowsiness?

$P(x < 110)$

$P(x \leq 109) = .8556$

The Mean and the Standard Deviation of a Binomial Random Variable

recall discrete r.v. in general

- The mean is $E(x) = \mu$

$$E(x) = n \cdot p$$

shortcut to get μ and σ in binomial r.v.

- The standard deviation is

$$\sigma = \sqrt{n \cdot p(1-p)}$$

par to calc $\mu + \sigma$

What are the mean and the standard deviation for the pharmaceutical company experiment?

$n = 500 \quad p = .20 \qquad E(x) = 500 \times .2 = 100$

$St \ dev = \sqrt{500 \cdot .20 (.80)} \approx 9$

Would it be unusual for 92 to 108 people in that experiment to experience drowsiness?

If pharm company's claim of 20 % drowsiness is true?

No, because 92 to 108 is w/in $\mu \pm 2\sigma$

Would it be unusual for more than 130 people in that experiment to experience drowsiness?

Yes beyond $\mu + 3\sigma$

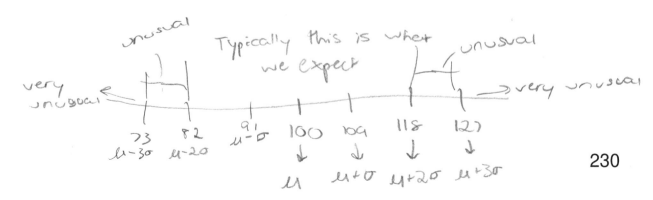

230

Claim: 75% of CT residents favor stricter gun control laws.
Test this claim.

Can I collect data that supports/refutes this claim?

I take an initial sample of 50 CT residents

Ask question: Y or N

$x = \#$ who say yes $n = 50$ $p = .75$

Create a model

x	$P(x=k)$
0	
1	
2	
:	
12	— a small value
:	
31	
:	
44	
:	
50	

Suppose I got $x = 12$

To see how unusual $x = 12$ is, calculate $P(x \le 12) \approx 0$

This is what I would expect if $p = .75$

It would be very weird to get $x \le 12$ if $p = .75$

Look at what we expect to get if $p = .75$

$\mu = n \cdot p = 50(.75) = 37.5$

$\sigma = \sqrt{n \cdot p (1-p)} \approx 3$

Make 2σ interval around μ

$37.5 \pm 2 \cdot 5$

37.5 ± 6

$31.5 \rightarrow 43.5$

Continuous Random Variables

Count data

↳ model: discrete model

Graph: possible x-values → as points on a # line

• • • • • • • •
x-values

Construct a pdf table

k-values

x							
P(x=k)							

Draw a prob histogram

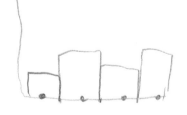

Each rectangle represents

P(x=k)

Measurement data

↳ model: continuous model

Graph: all possible x-values in an interval on a # line

[~~~~~~~~~~~~~]

Cannot construct pdf table b/c there's an infinite # of x-values

Draw a smooth curve

"Maybe a uniform "curve""

Normal curve

232

Continuous Random Variables

Notation for Probability in an Interval

↳ measurement data

    Always draw a graph

Example: heights of women

$\mu = 65''$
$\sigma = 2.5''$

65"

Every prob I calculate I must represent using an area

$P(67.5 \leq x \leq 70)$

↳ randomly selected woman

Suppose I want $\boxed{P(x = 68'')}$

68

I could calculate $P(67.5 \leq x \leq 68.5)$

↳ I say that this exact prob = 0

↳ The same as $P(67.5 < x < 68.5)$

Example 8.19: A bus arrives at a bus stop every 10 minutes. If a person arrives at the bus stop at a random time, how long will he or she have to wait for the next bus?

$X =$ waiting time → measurement data

model:
uniform
over the
interval
[0,10]

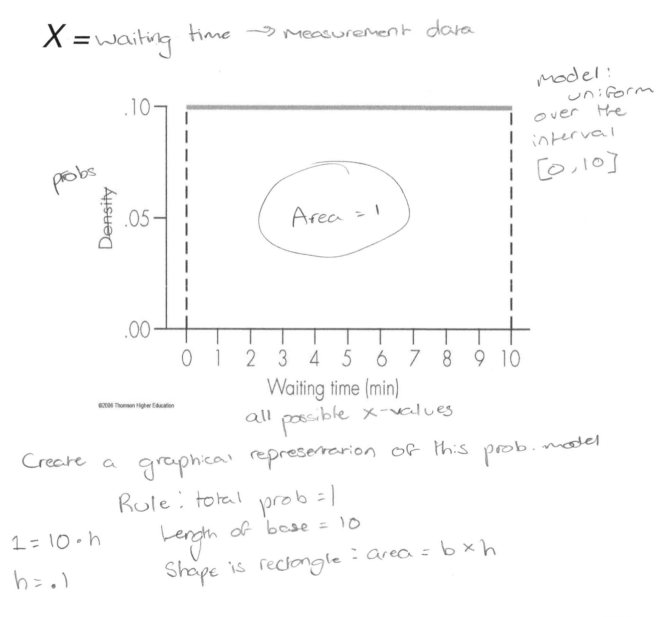

probs

Density

.10

.05

.00

0 1 2 3 4 5 6 7 8 9 10

Waiting time (min)

©2006 Thomson Higher Education

all possible x-values

Area = 1

Create a graphical representation of this prob. model

Rule: total prob = 1

Length of base = 10

Shape is rectangle: area = b × h

1 = 10 · h

h = .1

234

1. What is the probability that the waiting time is between 5 and 7 minutes?

$P(5 < x < 7)$

$P(5 \le x \le 7)$

Find the area $[5,7)$

$A = b \cdot h$

$.20 = 2 \times .10$

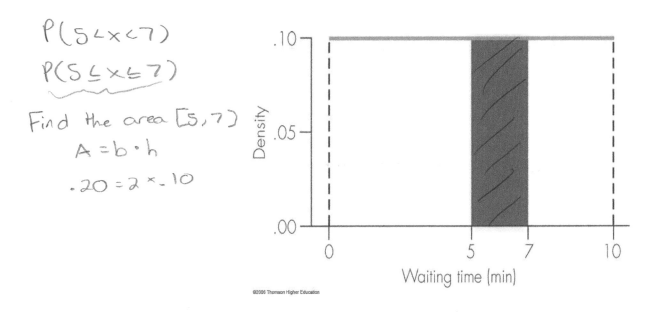

2. What is the probability that the waiting time is more than 7 minutes?

$P(x > 7)$

$P(x \ge 7)$

$A = b \cdot h$

$\downarrow$

$3 \times .10$

$.30$

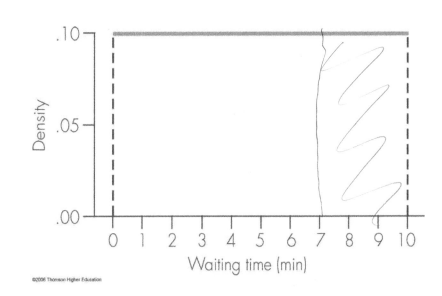

Generating Uniform Random Data

x: chemical reaction time in minutes

Run this experiment a large # of times and create a frequency histogram of data

Suppose I ran the experiment 258 times

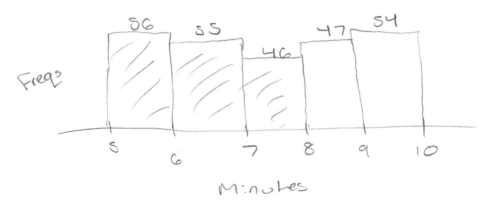

$$P(5 \leq x \leq 8) = \frac{56 + 55 + 46}{258} \approx .61$$

Creating a Theoretical Model for a Uniform Random Variable

X: chemical reaction time in minutes

X $\sim$ uniform model on interval $[5, 10]$

↓

follows

Prob ??

Set height so that the area = 1

$$A = b \times h$$
$$1 = 5 \times h$$
$$h = .2$$

$P(5 \leq x \leq 8)$

or $P(5 < x < 8)$ $3 \times .20 = \boxed{.60}$

Normal Random Variables

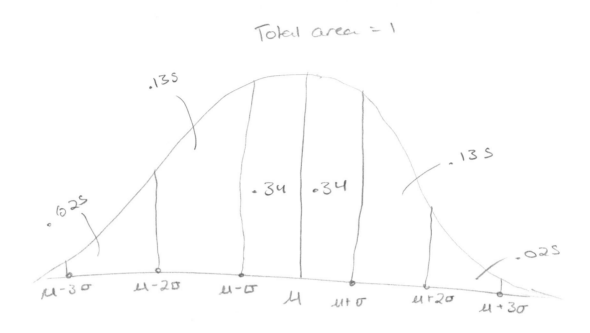

- # Features of Normal Curves:

  Total area = 1

  Curve is symmetric about μ

  Curve extends indefinitely to the right and to the left

  There is a very small amount of area beyond $\mu - 3\sigma$ and $\mu + 3\sigma$

Area Under the Normal Curve

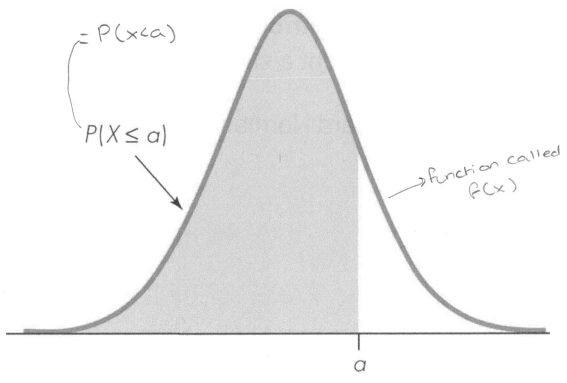

$= P(x < a)$

$P(X \leq a)$

→ function called $f(x)$

a

To find area:
① Standard normal table
＊ ② Calculator
③ $\int_{-\infty}^{a} f(x)\,dx$

Finding Probabilities for *z*-Scores

A normal random variable with mean $\mu = 0$ and standard deviation $\sigma = 1$ is said to have a **standard normal distribution.**

We use Z to represent a standard normal random variable

Table A.1, "Standard Normal Probabilities"

$$Z \sim N(0,1)$$

follows   normal μ σ

Standard normal random variable

Using Table A.1 to find probabilities on a Normal Curve

- Draw the curve
- Shade the area you want to find
- Use the Standard Normal Model in your calculator

$-1E99,$ comma
2nd ,

1. Find the area to the left of $Z = -1.62$

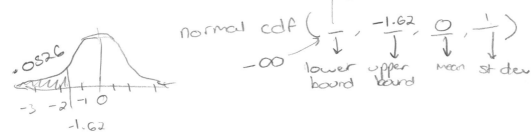

normal cdf $\left(\underset{-\infty}{\downarrow}, \underset{\substack{\text{lower} \\ \text{bound}}}{\overset{-1.62}{\downarrow}}, \underset{\substack{\text{upper} \\ \text{bound}}}{\downarrow}, \underset{\text{mean}}{\overset{0}{\downarrow}}, \underset{\text{st dev}}{\overset{1}{\downarrow}} \right)$

.0526

-3 -2 -1 0
-1.62

2. Find the area to the right of $Z = -2.05$

normalcdf $(-2.05, 1E99, 0, 1)$

.9798

-2.05   0

3. Find the area between $Z = .92$ and $Z = 2.67$

normal cdf $(.92, 2.67, 0, 1)$

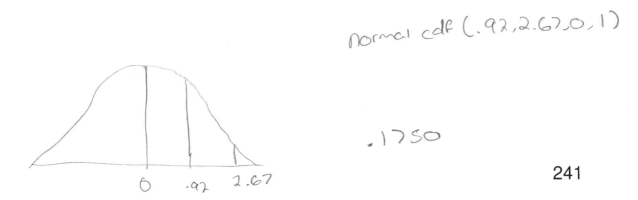

.1750

0   .92   2.67

241

Ex. Find the following probabilities for *X* = pulse rates for women, for which the mean is 75 bpm and the standard deviation is 8 bpm. Assume a normal distribution.

$X \sim N(75,8)$

1. $P(X \le 71)$

Suppose I select 1 woman

or $P(x < 71)$

normalcdf $(-1E99, 71, 75, 8)$

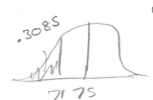

.3085

71 75

What does .3085 represent?

① Geometrically, it is the size of area under the curve

② It is the prob that, if I select 1 woman, her pulsrate satifies this condition

③ Proportion of population of women who satisfy this condition

2. $P(X \ge 85)$

75   85

normalcdf $(85, 1E99, 75, 8)$
.1056

3. $P(59 \le X \le 95)$

59 75   95

normal cdf $(59, 95, 75, 8)$
.9710

242

- What are the cutoff points for the middle 50% for the systolic blood pressure of men aged 18 to 29 years?

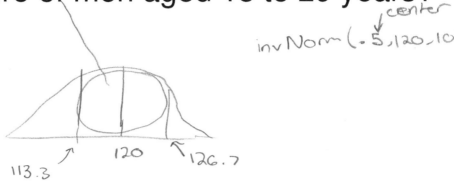

center

invNorm (.5,120,10)

113.3   120   126.7

- What are the cutoff points for the middle 80% for the systolic blood pressure of men aged 18 to 29 years?

invNorm (.8,120,10)

107.2   132.8

Find cutoff point for top 10%

.10

?

invNorm (.10,120,10) = 132.8

right

Finding percentiles or proportions or probabilities

These are called inverse problems

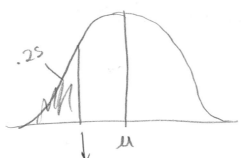

.25

μ

This point is the 25th percentile

Probability statement

$$P(x \leq \underline{}) = .25$$

Compare this to type I problem!

$$P(x \geq 85) = \underline{}$$

Type 2 normal problem → start w/ a left area under the curve and find x-value

Called an inverse problem

X = BP of males aged 18-29

What value of x(BP) is the 75% percentile?

Prob Statement

$$P(x \leq \underline{}) = 75$$
$$?$$

Suppose $X \sim N(120, 10)$

.75

126.7

invNorm (area, μ, σ)   invNorm (.75, 120, 10)
         ↓
   choose left or
     right area

Examples of Binompdf and Binomcdf

   x: # of success $n = 20$ $p = .10$

a. P(exactly 3 successes) binompdf(20, .1, 3)

b. P(fewer than 4 successes) binomcdf(20 .1, 3)
        $P(x < 4)$

c. P(more than 5 successes) 1 − binomcdf(20, .1, 5)
        $P(x > 5)$ means _, 6, 7, ... 20

d. P(at least 4 successes) 1 − binomcdf(20, .1, 3)
        $P(x \geq 4)$ means 4, 5, 6 20

e. More than 2 but less than 8
                    binomcdf(20, .1, 7) − binomcdf(20, .1, 2)

f. between 1 and 4 inclusive
        binomcdf(20, .10, 4) − binomcdf(20, .1, 0)

246

Chapter 9:
Understanding Sampling Distributions

Ch 7 Basic probability rules

Ch 8 Prob models/distributions

We use these models to describe how a
random variable, X, behaves
We need these underlying models in our analysis
of data

Ex- random variable, X
measurement data

How does X behave?

① Center = μ
② Spread = σ
③ Shape = ? — normal
— uniform
other

Ex. X → count data
yes/no data then our
model is binomial
How does X behave?

① n # of trials
② p = prob of success

From Populations to Samples to Populations

generalize

Statistical inference

① Start with a question about a population

What is avg starting salary of teachers in CT?

How do ppl feel about gun control laws? For/against

② Take a random sample and collect data on the sample units

③ Use the sample data to answer questions about the population

249

Parameter vs. Statistic

Parameter

Statistic

numerical characteristic of a population

↓

unknown value w/o having data from entire population

But it is a fixed value

numerical characteristic of a sample

It is a known value, but it varies from sample to sample

Estimates

$$\mu \longleftarrow \bar{x}$$

$$\sigma \longleftarrow s$$

$$p \longleftarrow \hat{p} \leftarrow \text{sample proportion}$$
$$p\text{-hat}$$

Key Fact about a Sample Statistic

- If two or more different samples are taken from the same population, the sample statistics most likely will be different for those samples

$$\overline{X}_1 \neq \overline{X}_2 \neq \overline{X}_3 \neq \overline{X}_4 \cdots$$

$$\hat{p}_1 \neq \hat{p}_2 \cdots$$

- This means that values of a sample statistic vary, that is a statistic is also a random variable

such as $\overline{X}$ or $\hat{p}$

the statistic varies, but it varies according to an underlying pattern

Statistical Inference

- The conclusions we make about population parameters on the basis of sample statistics are called **statistical inference**

① (Confidence Intervals)

② (Hypothesis Testing)

Confidence Interval

- **Example:** A study on global warming conducted by the Connecticut Center for Survey Research found that 45% of the 501 individuals polled felt that it was possible for individuals to do something about global warming.

x = # who said yes

$\dfrac{x}{501}$ = 45% or .45 $\longrightarrow$ $\hat{p} \rightarrow$ sample proportion

Generalize from sample back to population

Want to use $\hat{p}$ to estimate p

Problem: $\hat{p}$ probably $\neq p$ exactly

Solution: to estimate p, $\hat{p} \pm$ margin of error

need to know how $\hat{p}$s behave

Hypothesis Testing
(Significance Testing)

- **Example:** A study was designed to test a new blood pressure drug. Pharmaceutical company claims BP will drop by 20 points on average. In a sample of 50 participants with high blood pressure, the drug was found to lower blood pressure by 15 points on average.

$\bar{x} = 15$

↓ is random variable, so it varies from sample to sample

Does this value of $\bar{x} = 15$ negate what the drug company claims?

How do $\bar{x}$s behave?

The Statistical Research Method

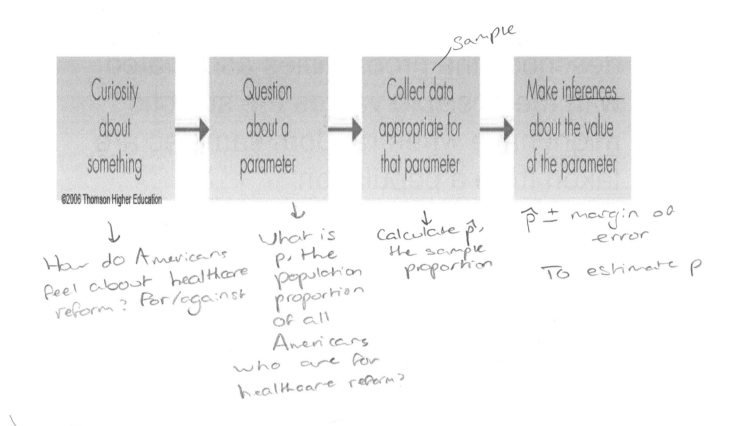

Sample

| Curiosity about something | Question about a parameter | Collect data appropriate for that parameter | Make <u>inferences</u> about the value of the parameter |

©2006 Thomson Higher Education

↓
How do Americans feel about healthcare reform? For/against

↓
What is p, the population proportion of all Americans who are for healthcare reform?

↓
Calculate p̂, the sample proportion

p̂ ± margin of error

To estimate p

Do male nurses earn more than female nurses

$\mu_m > \mu_F$

$\overline{x}_m$ and $\overline{x}_F$

Does my data support the claim that $\overline{x}_m > \overline{x}_F$?

Behavior $\overline{x}$

- The sampling distribution for a statistic $^{like}_{\overline{x}}$ describes the probabilities associated with the possible values the statistic might have when random samples are taken from a population

How do $\overline{x}_s$ vary?

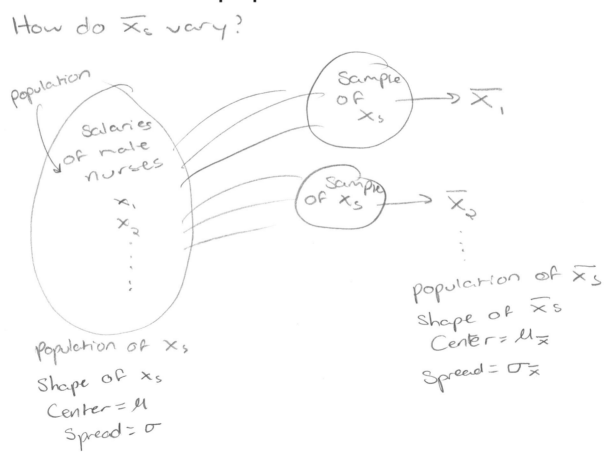

Population

Salaries of male nurses

x_1

x_2

$\vdots$

Sample of x_s $\longrightarrow \overline{x}_1$

Sample of x_s $\longrightarrow \overline{x}_2$

Population of x_s

Shape of x_s

Center = μ

Spread = σ

Population of $\overline{x}_s$

Shape of $\overline{x}_s$

Center = $\mu_{\overline{x}}$

Spread = $\sigma_{\overline{x}}$

Sampling Distribution

- Three key questions about a sampling *behavior* distribution for a sample statistic: *like $\bar{x}$*

  - What is the center of the sampling distribution? $\mu_{\bar{x}}$ *(center of $\bar{x}$s)*

  - What is the spread of the sampling distribution? $\sigma_{\bar{x}}$

  - What is the shape of the sampling distribution? *In particular, is it normal or not?*

257

Sampling Distribution for $\overline{X}$

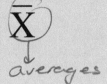

averages

- Suppose we are interested in estimating the mean, μ, of a population

- Procedure for estimating μ:
  - Take a sample from the population and calculate the sample mean $\rightarrow \overline{x}$
  - Use the **sample mean** to estimate the **population mean**

  Problem: most likely $\overline{x}$ does not equal μ exactly

- Question: How close will the **sample mean** be to the **population mean?**

  To answer this we need to know how $\overline{x}$s behave

Behavior

Sampling Distribution for the Sample Mean $\overline{x}_s$
Data: Cholesterol Readings from a Population of 50 Women at a clinic

x_s:

Population

146 180 103 183 97 122 257 99 168 188

107 202 277 52 212 222 222 148 232 69

104 121 77 136 203 36 142 130 112 54

118 103 47 219 161 87 149 169 178 79

148 106 217 88 253 61 197 240 133 159

- $\mu = 145$ $\sigma = 60$

- *Use your random number generator to take a sample of 20 data points from the population shown here. Circle your 20 data points.*

For your sample of 20 women, calculate the mean.

$\bar{x} = 136$ compare those $\mu = 145$

$s = 64$ to $\sigma = 60$

s

1 random
sample of
size $n = 20$

Create a set of 25 sample means.

25 random samples of size $n = 20$

136	139	154	141	161
158	147	133	151	142
132	148	148	151	139
166	132	143	147	137
151	118	146	131	143

$\bar{x}_s$

Sampling Distribution for the Sample Mean

For your set of 25 sample means, find the mean and standard deviation.

How do these $\bar{x}$s behave?

    Center of 25 $\bar{x}$s : 144

    St dev of $\bar{x}$s : 10.6

Center of my $\bar{x}$s is close to population mean of 140

St dev of $\bar{x}$s is much smaller then pop St dev of 60

$$\mu_{\bar{x}} = \mu \quad \text{and} \quad \sigma_{\bar{x}} = \sqrt{\frac{N-n}{N-1}} \cdot \frac{\sigma}{\sqrt{n}}$$

≈ 1

For example $N = 10000$ close to

                 $n = 20$ 1 when N

$\sqrt{\frac{10000-20}{10000-1}} \approx 1$ is large

Population Distribution for X vs. Sampling Distribution for $\bar{x}$

individual values in a population

- Given a population with the following characteristics:
  Xs
  ① – Population mean, $\mu = 80$
  ② – Population standard deviation, $\sigma = 5$
  – Population distribution is <u>normal</u>

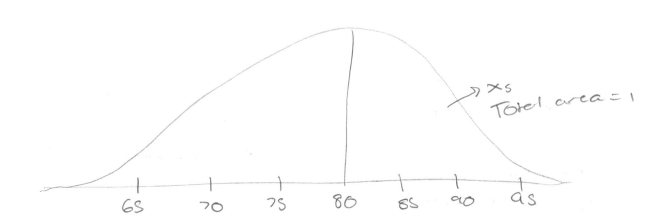

Xs
Total area = 1

65   70   75   80   85   90   95

Sampling Distribution for the Sample Mean

- Take repeated samples of size 25 from this normal population and calculate the sample mean for each sample of size 25 $\downarrow_{\overline{x}}$

- Characteristics of the sampling distribution: → population of $\overline{x}_s$

① $\mu_{\overline{x}} = \mu = 80$

② $\sigma_{\overline{x}} \approx \dfrac{\sigma}{\sqrt{n}} = \dfrac{5}{\sqrt{25}} = 1$

③ $\overline{x}_s$ Normal

because x_s are normal

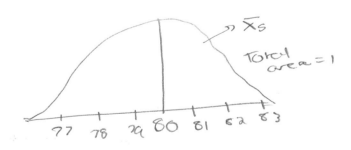

» $\overline{x}_s$

Total area = 1

77 78 79 80 81 82 83

Sampling Distribution for $\bar{x}$

Start w/ a population of xs
   w/ mean $= \mu$, st dev $= \sigma$

Take samples of size n
Calculate $\bar{x}$ for each sample
   These $\bar{x}$s make

3 Questions:

① What is $\mu_{\bar{x}}$? $= \mu$

② What is $\sigma_{\bar{x}}$? $\approx \dfrac{\sigma}{\sqrt{n}}$

③ What is shape of $\bar{x}$s?
   a) If xs are normal, so are $\bar{x}$s
   b) If xs are not normal, apply Central Limit
       Theorem (CLT)
         • $\bar{x}$s will be approximately normal in
            shape regardless of shape of xs provided
            our sample size is "large enough"

         our rule: $n \geq 30$

Probability Distribution of $\boxed{X}$
and
Sampling Distribution of $\overline{X}$

- **Example:** Tiger Woods (who many consider one of the best golfer of all time) typically hit his drives more than 300 yds. Data from two of his PGA tours showed the average distance he hit his driver was 305 yds with a standard deviation of 15 yds. A graph of the data indicated a normal distribution.

What is the probability that he hits a drive of at least 312 yds?

$x = $ driving distance of individual drives

$x \sim N(305, 15)$

$P(x \geq 312)$

normalcdf $(312, 1E99, 305, 15) = .3204$

Probability Distribution of X
and
Sampling Distribution of $\bar{x}$

- **Example:** Suppose we look at a sample of nine of his drives. What is the probability that the **sample average** is at least 312 yds?

$\downarrow$
$\bar{x}$

$P(\bar{x} \geq 312)$

Behavior of $\bar{x}$s:

$\dfrac{\sigma}{\sqrt{n}}$

$\bar{x} \sim N(u_{\bar{x}}, \sigma_{\bar{x}})$

$\downarrow$

b/c x_s are normal

$\rho \bar{x}_s$

305   312

$305 \quad \dfrac{15}{\sqrt{9}}$

$\text{normalcdf}\left(312, 1E99, 305, \dfrac{15}{\sqrt{9}}\right) = .0808$

Sampling Distribution for $\bar{x}$

- The Central Limit Theorem applies to the sampling distribution of the sample mean in cases where the underlying population is not normally distributed and the observations are independent

- The Central Limit Theorem states that the sampling distribution of the sample mean for the sample of independent observations is approximately normal (regardless of the shape of the parent population) provided the sample size is sufficiently large.

- Practical guide: $n \geq 30$

Probability Distribution of X
and
Sampling Distribution of $\overline{x}$

- **Example:** Tiger Woods (revisited). Data from his last two PGA tours showed the average distance he hit his drive was 305 yds with a standard deviation of 15 yds. A graph of the data indicated a **skewed** distribution.

  What is the probability that he hits a drive of at least 312 yds?

X: individual drives

X ~ skewed(305, 15)

P(x ≥ 312) :⌣

Can't use normalcdf unless
we have normal data

- **Example:** Tiger Woods (revisited).

  Suppose we look at a sample of nine of his drives. What is the probability that the **sample average** is at least 312 yds?

  We say $X \sim$ skewed $(305, 15)$

  $p(\overline{x} \geq 312)$:(

  can't use normalcdf because

  ① xs aren't normal

  ② CLT doesn't apply because $n < 30$

Probability Distribution of X
and
Sampling Distribution of $\bar{x}$

- **Example:** Tiger Woods (revisited).

  Suppose we look at a sample of thirty of his drives. What is the probability that the **sample average** is at least 312 yds?

  $X \sim$ skewed$(305, 15)$

  $P(\bar{x} \geq 312) \Rightarrow$ ☺

  Now CLT applies because
  ① x_s aren't normal
  ② n is at least 30
  → normalcdf$(312, 1E99, 305, \frac{15}{\sqrt{30}}) = .0063$

Probability Distribution of X
and
Sampling Distribution of $\overline{x}$

- **Example**: The scores of High School students on a standardized test to measure mathematical aptitude had a mean of 62 and a standard deviation of 14.7. The distribution of scores was roughly Normal.

What is the approximate probability that a single student randomly chosen from all those taking the test scored 69 or higher?

$P(x \geq 69)$ $X \sim N(62, 14.7)$

normalcdf $(69, 1E99, 62, 14.7) = .3170$

Probability Distribution of X
and
Sampling Distribution of $\overline{x}$

- **Example:** Take a random sample of 50 students who took the test. What is the approximate probability that the mean scores of these students is 69 or higher?

$P(\overline{x} \geq 69)$

$\overline{x} \sim N(62, 14.7/50)$

↓
because Xs
are N

$\text{normalcdf}(69, 1E99, 62, 14.7/50) = .00038$

Probability Distribution of X
And
Sampling Distribution of $\bar{x}$

- **Example**: An insurance company's records for the year 2005 indicate that the average loss from water damage to homes in Louisiana was $550 with a standard deviation of $2000. The distribution of losses is strongly right-skewed with many policies in northern Louisiana having $0 loss. Closer to the shoreline, the losses were quite large. If the company sells 10,000 $\rightarrow$ n policies this year, what is the approximate probability that the average loss will be greater than $600. The company assumes a year similar to 2005 in terms of weather.

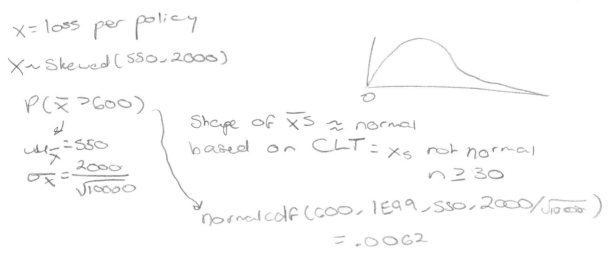

$x = $ loss per policy

$X \sim$ Skewed $(550, 2000)$

$P(\bar{x} > 600)$

$\mu_{\bar{x}} = 550$

$\sigma_{\bar{x}} = \dfrac{2000}{\sqrt{10000}}$

Shape of $\bar{x}$s $\approx$ normal based on CLT = xs not normal

$n \geq 30$

normalcdf $(600, 1E99, 550, 2000/\sqrt{10000})$

$= .0062$

Standard Error of the Mean

s estimates σ

- In practice, the population standard deviation, σ, is rarely known. The sample standard deviation, (s), is used to estimate σ

  We need to estimate $\sigma_{\bar{x}}$

  $\boxed{\sigma_{\bar{x}}} \approx \frac{\sigma}{\sqrt{n}}$ → rarely known

  replace σ in the formula w/ s, sample st dev

- The **standard error of the mean** is defined as:

$$s.e.(\bar{x}) = \frac{s}{\sqrt{n}}$$

  We estimate $\boxed{\sigma_{\bar{x}}}$ using $\frac{s}{\sqrt{n}}$

  called st dev of $\bar{x}$s

Increasing the Size of the Sample

How does n affect behavior of $\bar{x}s$?

Suppose: population of x_s $X \sim N(8, 5)$

Take samples of size $n = 25$ and calculate $\bar{x}s$

How do $\bar{x}s$ behave?

$\bar{X} \sim N(8, \frac{5}{\sqrt{25}})$

$\bar{X} \sim N(8, 1)$

Suppose I take samples of size $n = 100$

$\bar{X} \sim N(8, \frac{5}{\sqrt{100}})$

$\bar{X} \sim N(8, 0.5)$

Both cases, area under curve = 1

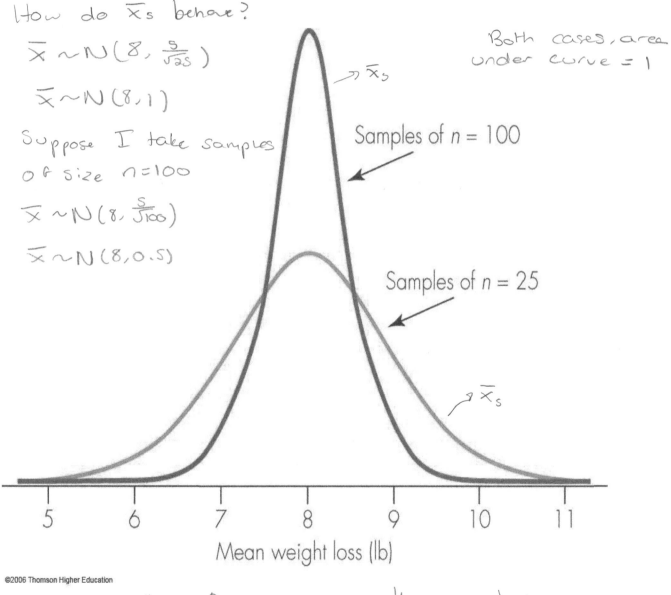

$\bar{x}s$

Samples of $n = 100$

Samples of $n = 25$

$\bar{x}s$

Mean weight loss (lb)

5   6   7   8   9   10   11

As $n \uparrow$, $\mu_{\bar{x}}$ remains the same but $\sigma_{\bar{x}} \downarrow$

275

Minitab Ch 7 Problem

Last question

shape
unknown

$X \longrightarrow$ speeds (mph) of cars on a highway

Lots of data $\mu = 62, \sigma = 5$
tend to

Police: Do ppl drive Faster on holiday weekends?

Their study: sample of speeds of cars on a
holiday weekend $n = 50, \bar{x} = 66$

Is getting $\bar{x} = 66$ enough for police to conclude
into
that people drive faster on holiday weekends?

To answer this, we start by assuming that μ still equals
is
62 on holiday weekends. Where is $\bar{x}$ of 66 in relation
to $\mu = 62$? We need to know how $\bar{x}$s behave.

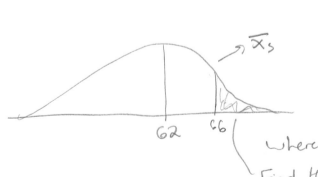

$\mu_{\bar{x}} = 62$
$\sigma_{\bar{x}} = 5/\sqrt{50}$

Shape of $\bar{x}_s \sim N$
b/c CLT

Where does 66 fall?
Find the size of this area
normal cdf $(66, 1E99, 62, 5/\sqrt{50})$
≈ 0

So, $P(\bar{x} \geq 66)$ if μ still $= 62 \quad \approx 0$

It would be rlly unlikely to get an $\bar{x}$ of 66 or
higher if μ does still $= 62$, since 66 is our $\bar{x}$ value,
we conclude μ must not $= 62$

276

Sampling Distribution for $\hat{p}$

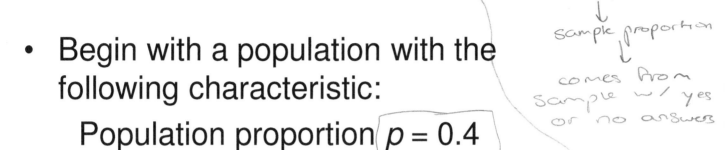

random variable called $\hat{p}$

↓

sample proportion

↓

comes from sample w/ yes or no answers

- Begin with a population with the following characteristic:

  Population proportion $p = 0.4$

- **Example:** Suppose we know that the proportion of the population with Type A Blood is 0.4.

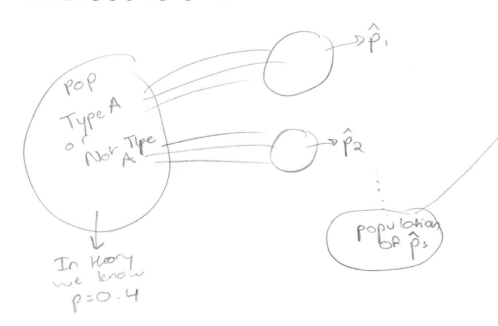

POP
Type A
or
Not Type A

In theory we know $p = 0.4$

$\to \hat{p}_1$

$\to \hat{p}_2$

population of $\hat{p}$s

277

Sampling Distribution for the Sample Proportion

- Take repeated samples from the population and calculate the sample proportion $\hat{p}$ for each sample

- Characteristics of the sampling distribution: of $\hat{p}$s

$$\mu_{\hat{p}} = p = 0.4$$

① Center Mean$(\hat{p})$ = proportion = $p = 0.4$

$\sigma_{\hat{p}}$

Spread Standard deviation = $s.d.(\hat{p}) = \sqrt{\dfrac{p(1-p)}{n}}$

Shape : approximately normal (provided the sample size, n, is sufficiently large)

We will always satisfy this criteria of normality

Sampling Distribution for the Sample Proportion

$p \to$ population proportion

- **Example:** Suppose that of all voters in the U.S., 40% are in favor of candidate A. Pollsters take samples of 2400 voters and calculate the sample proportion, $\hat{p}$, for each sample

Describe the sampling distribution of the sample proportion

① Center of $\hat{p}$s: $\mu_{\hat{p}} = p = 0.4$

② Spread of $\hat{p}$s: $\sigma_{\hat{p}} = \sqrt{\frac{p(1-p)}{n}} = \sqrt{\frac{.4(1-.4)}{2400}} = .01$

③ Shape of $\hat{p}$s: $\approx$ normal since n is large

if $p = .4$, for samples of size $n = 2400$, $\hat{p}$ should fall in the range .37 to .43

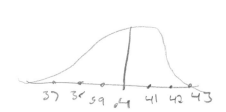

37 38 39 .4 41 42 43

Standard Error of the Sample Proportion

In practice, the population proportion, p, is rarely known. *You are trying to estimate it*

The sample proportion, $\hat{p}$, is used to estimate the population proportion, p.

So our standard dev

$$\sigma_{\hat{p}} = \sqrt{\frac{p(1-p)}{n}}$$

is unknown

$\parallel$

Estimate $\sigma_{\hat{p}}$ using

The standard error of $\hat{p}$ is defined as: $\sqrt{\dfrac{\hat{p}(1-\hat{p})}{n}}$

Chapter 10 - Part 1
Estimating a Proportion with a Confidence Interval

yes or no

p

What proportion of all Americans think Obamacare is working?

Take sample of size n

Calculate $\hat{p}$ → sample proportion

$$\frac{\# \text{ of yes}}{n}$$

Suppose we get $\hat{p} = .10$

Do you think that $p = .10$ exactly?

Probably not

Why? $\hat{p}$ is a random variable

To est. p: $\hat{p} \pm \underline{\text{something}}$

Sampling Distributions
and Confidence Intervals –ch.10

–ch.9

theoretical ch.

- The basic idea of a **sampling distribution** is to use knowledge of the population to describe possible sample values. Suppose in theory, we know p. Answer the question: how do $\hat{p}$'s behave?

ch.9

random variable

- The basic idea of a **confidence interval** is to use information from a sample to estimate a population value.

p   *$\hat{p}$*

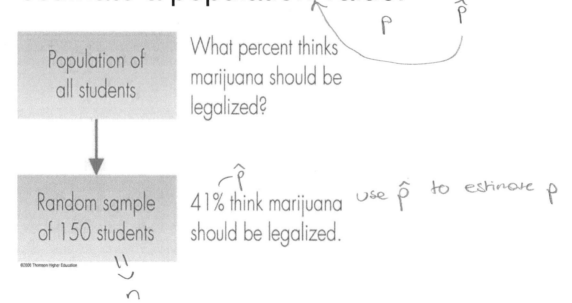

Population of all students

What percent thinks marijuana should be legalized?

Random sample of 150 students

$\hat{p}$
41% think marijuana should be legalized.

use $\hat{p}$ to estimate p

©2006 Thomson Higher Education

$\dfrac{n}{}$

Population Parameters and Sample Statistics

Estimate p (population parameter)
Use $\hat{p}$ (sample statistic)

$$\hat{p} = \frac{\text{\# of people in sample who said yes}}{\text{sample size}}$$

estimate p:

$\hat{p} \pm$ margin of error

(lower bound, upper bound)

A confidence interval consists of values computed from sample data that is likely to include the true population value.

• Why do we use an interval to estimate the true value of a population parameter?

because $\hat{p}$ probably $\neq$ p exactly

$$\underline{\text{point estimate}} \pm \text{margin of error}$$

$\hat{p} \pm$

$.10 \pm .0001 \rightarrow$ probably this interval isn't better @ estimating p than $\hat{p}$ itself

$.10 \pm .50 \rightarrow$ too wide to be useful for estimating p

Idea of a Confidence Interval for p

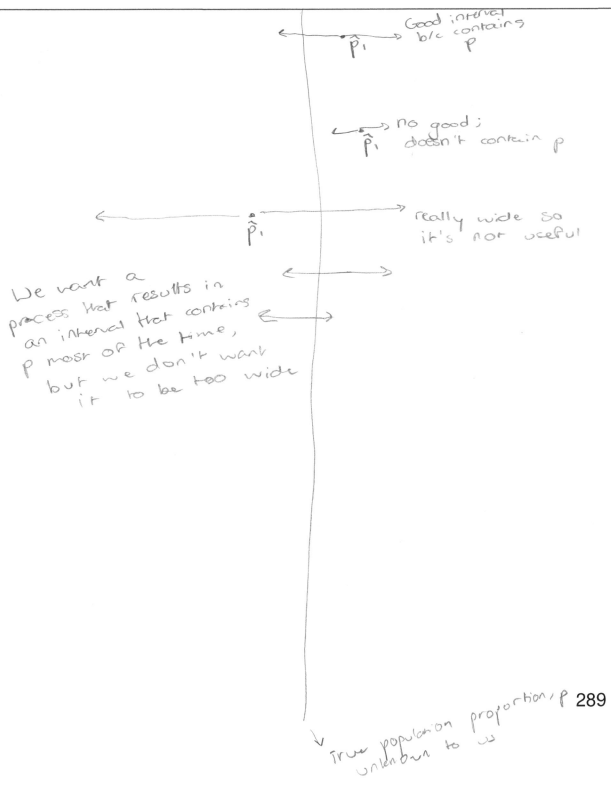

Good interval b/c contains p

$\hat{p}_1$

no good; doesn't contain p

$\hat{p}_1$

really wide so it's not useful

$\hat{p}_1$

We want a process that results in an interval that contains p most of the time, but we don't want it to be too wide

True population proportion, p — unknown to us

289

$\hat{p} \pm$ margin of error

To determine moe, start w/ behavior of $\hat{p}$'s

Suppose we actually know what the real value of p is (population proportion)

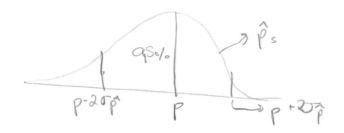

Empirical rule: 95% of data lies w/in 2 st devs of mean

95% of the time, a sample proportion will fall in the interval $[p - 2\sigma_{\hat{p}}, p + 2\sigma_{\hat{p}}]$

I know $\hat{p}_s \sim N\left(p, \sqrt{\frac{p(1-p)}{n}}\right)$

Suppose I make moe = $\boxed{2\sigma_{\hat{p}}}$

$2\sigma_{\hat{p}} = 2\sqrt{\frac{p(1-p)}{n}}$

290

A **confidence interval** or an **interval estimate** can be expressed as

point estimate $\pm$ multiplier $\times$ standard error

- 95% Confidence interval for one population proportion $\hat{p}$ $\pm$ 2 $s.e(\hat{p})$ *estimate of st dev of $\hat{p}$*

$$\hat{p} \pm 1.96 \cdot \sqrt{\frac{\hat{p}(1-\hat{p})}{n}}$$

more preciese than 2

- **Example 10.2:** In April, 883 randomly selected adults were surveyed about allergies. Thirty-six percent answered "yes" to the question, "Are you allergic to anything?" Estimate p, the proportion of all adults who have allergies using a 95% confidence interval.

$n = 883$ $\hat{p} = .36$

$.36 \pm 1.96 \sqrt{\frac{.36(1-.36)}{883}}$

$.36 \pm .032$

$.36 - .032$

$.36 + .032$

$\approx 33\%$ to 39%

$(.328, .392)$

291

Interpreting the Confidence Level

Based on our sample, we have created a 95% confidence interval that states that somewhere between 33% and 39% of all Americans suffer from allergies.

Are we certain that this interval actually does contain p? NO

All we know is that we used a process that will contain p 95% of the time

For a confidence interval, the **confidence level** is the relative frequency or probability that the procedure will provide intervals including the population parameter, under a large number of replications.

really but unknown values of p

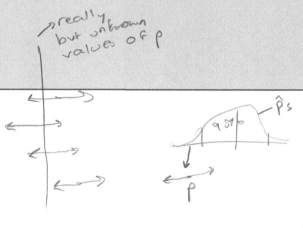

Finding the Multiplier z^*

•The multiplier z^* is the standardized score such that the area between $-z^*$ and $+z^*$ under the standard normal curve corresponds to the desired confidence level. C.I. in general for p. population proportion

$$\hat{p} \pm z^* \sqrt{\frac{\hat{p}(1-\hat{p})}{n}}$$

Typical confidence levels:
90%
95% → typically used
98%
99%
99.9%

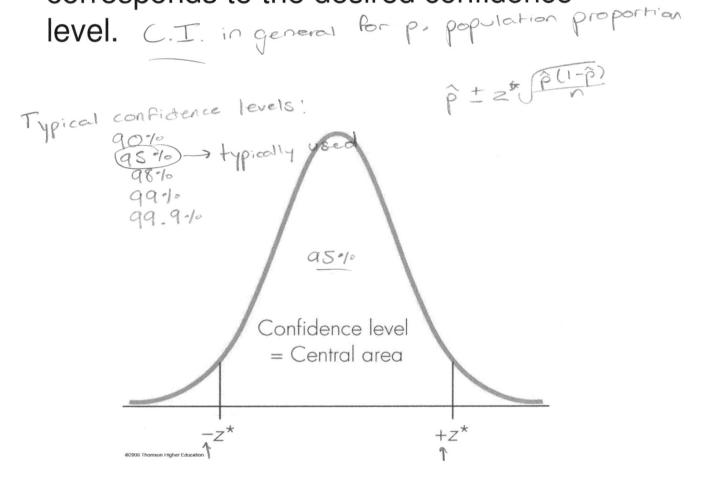

95%

Confidence level
= Central area

$-z^*$ $+z^*$

©2006 Thomson Higher Education

Table 10.1 Confidence Intervals for a Population Proportion

Confidence Level	Multiplier (z^*)	Confidence Interval
90	1.645 or 1.65	$\hat{p} \pm 1.65$ standard errors
(95)	(1.960, sometimes rounded to 2	$\hat{p} \pm 2$ standard errors
98	2.326 or 2.33	$\hat{p} \pm 2.33$ standard errors
99	2.576 or 2.58	$\hat{p} \pm 2.58$ standard errors

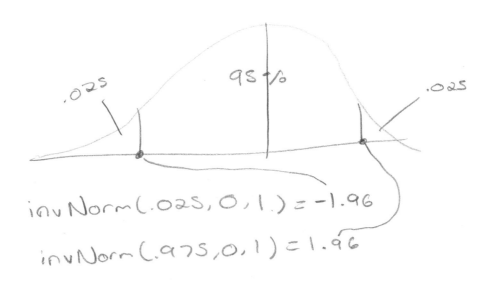

.025   95%   .025

invNorm(.025, 0, 1) = -1.96

invNorm(.975, 0, 1) = 1.96

Example 10.3: In a 2008 survey of 1003 randomly selected Americans, 56% answered that it is either very likely or Somewhat likely that there is intelligent Life on other planets.

CI

$\hat{p} \pm moe$

$z^* \cdot \sqrt{\frac{\hat{p}(1-\hat{p})}{n}}$

means that process I am using to create confidence interval that actually contains p 90 times out of 100

p

1. Calculate a 90% confidence interval for the proportion of all Americans who believe that there is most likely intelligent life on other planets.

p

x: # who think there is intelligent life on other planets

$n = 1003$

$\hat{p} = .56 = \frac{x}{n} \rightarrow 1003$

$x = .56 \cdot 1003$

stat → Test
#1-6 Hypothesis tests
#7-8 CIs
A: 1 PropZint

x: .56(1003) → 562

n: 1003

C-level: .9

$\hat{p} = .5603$

(.5345, .5861)
lower   upper

moe: $\frac{u - L}{2} =$

.0258

you get 561.68 → this must be converted to nearest whole #: 562

295

2. Calculate a 99% confidence interval.

$(0.520, 0.601)$ or $.56 \pm .0405$

$\hat{p} = .56$

$MOE = \dfrac{.601 - .520}{2} = .0405$

3. Calculate a 95% confidence interval.

$(.530, .591)$

$\hat{p} = .56$

$MOE = \dfrac{.591 - .530}{2} = .0305$

- ## Summary:
  ## 90% interval

  $\hat{p} \pm MOE \longrightarrow z^* \cdot \sqrt{\dfrac{\hat{p}(1-\hat{p})}{n}}$

  $(\_,\_)$ $.56 \pm .026$

  ## 95% interval $.56 \pm .031$
  $(\_,\_)$

  ## 99% interval $.56 \pm .041$
  $(\_,\_)$

opposing forces   2 things to notice $.9, .95, .99$

① As c-level ↑, the width of c interval ↑
    (gets wider)

② As c-level ↑, the chance of creating
an interval that does not contain
    p ↓ (that's good)

Confidence Interval for a Population Proportion p

$$\widehat{p} \pm z^* \sqrt{\frac{\widehat{p}(1-\widehat{p})}{n}}$$

A: 1 Prop Z int

$\widehat{p} = \frac{x}{n}$ ✓

where

$\widehat{p}$ is the sample proportion

$z*$ denotes the multiplier

$\sqrt{\dfrac{\widehat{p}(1-\widehat{p})}{n}}$ is the estimated standard

error of the sample proportion, $\widehat{p}$

(lower , upper) ⟵

I believe that p, pop. proportion, falls

Also written $\widehat{p} \pm MOE$ $\dfrac{upper - lower}{2}$

Ex: In a poll done by Princeton Survey Research Associates in October 1998, 422 of 753 randomly sampled American adults answered "yes" to the question "Do you personally believe that abortion is wrong?"

1. Calculate a 99% confidence interval for the October 1998 percentage of all Americans who believed abortion was wrong.

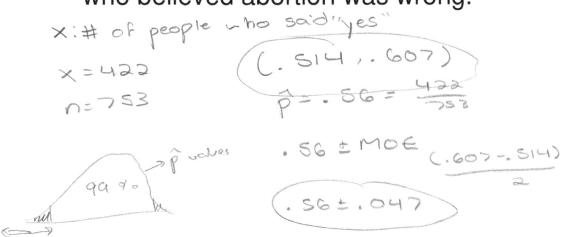

X: # of people who said "yes"

$x = 422$

$n = 753$

$(.514 , .607)$

$\hat{p} = .56 = \frac{422}{753}$

99% → $\hat{p}$ values

$.56 \pm MOE$

$\frac{(.607 - .514)}{2}$

$.56 \pm .047$

2. On the basis of this confidence interval, is it reasonable to conclude that in October 1998 more than half of all Americans thought that abortion was wrong?

$> .50$

Yes; the entire interval lies above .50
Are we certain that the true proportion is
> .5? No! All we know is that we used
a process that results in an interval that
contains p 99% of the time

299

Some Factors That Affect the Width of a Confidence Interval

Estimate p: $\widehat{p} \pm z^* \sqrt{\dfrac{\widehat{p}(1-\widehat{p})}{n}}$ MOE → determines width of CI

1. z^* is determined by c-level
   As c-level ↑, z^* ↑

2. $\widehat{p}$: sample proportion → we cannot control

3. n: sample size
   As n ↑, width ↓
   More data is always better b/c width of
   CI ↓ as n ↑

How much data do I actually need?

This can be determined by

   ① Confidence level

   ② Max size of MOE ⟩ you decide on

Start w/ MOE part of CI

   $z^* \sqrt{\frac{\hat{p}(1-\hat{p})}{n}}$ = set to a max MOE, called E

   $z^* \sqrt{\frac{\hat{p}(1-\hat{p})}{n}} = E$

Solve for n: $n = \hat{p}(1-\hat{p}\left(\frac{z^*}{E}\right)^2$

z-value
depends on C-level
I decide

↘ max error in decimal form

$\hat{p}$:

   ① use an estimate from a previous study

or

   ② use a "middle of the road" value of 0.5

Example: Suppose you want to conduct a survey now to find out what proportion of American adults believe that abortion is wrong. How large a sample would you need if you want a margin of error no greater than 5 percentage points with a confidence level of 90%?   ↓ $_{\text{Max error}}$
$.05$

a)   With no prior knowledge of the proportion

$$n = \hat{p}(1-\hat{p})\left(\frac{Z^*}{E}\right)^2$$

$$= (.5)(.5)\left(\frac{1.645}{.05}\right)^2 = 270.6 \rightarrow 271$$

b)   Using the proportion from the 1998 study

$$n = \hat{p}(1-\hat{p})\left(\frac{Z^*}{E}\right)^2$$

$$.56(1-.56)\left(\frac{1.645}{.05}\right)^2 =$$

From 1998: .56

$$266.7$$
$$\downarrow$$
$$n = 267$$

Case Study 10.2: Nicotine Patches Versus Zyban

- Is it reasonable to conclude that two population proportions are different from each other?

- Many people who are trying to quit smoking use nicotine patches to ease nicotine withdrawal symptoms. Medical researchers have begun to investigate whether the use of an antidepressant medication might be a more effective aid to those attempting to give up cigarettes. Dr. Douglas Jorenby and colleagues compared the effectiveness of nicotine patches to the effectiveness of the antidepressant buproprion (Zyban).

Table 10.3 displays, for each treatment group, an approximate 95% confidence interval for the proportion not smoking six months after the start of the experiment.

Table 10.3 95% Confidence Intervals for Proportion Not Smoking after Six Months

Treatment	Subjects	Proportion Not Smoking	Approx. 95% CI
Placebo only	160	.188	.13 to .25
Nicotine patch	244	.213	.16 to .26
Zyban	244	.348	.29 to .41
Zyban and nicotine patch	245	.388	.33 to .44

©2006 Thomson Higher Education

$\hat{p}$s

CIs for P, pop. proportion

Figure 10.4 shows the 95% confidence interval graphically

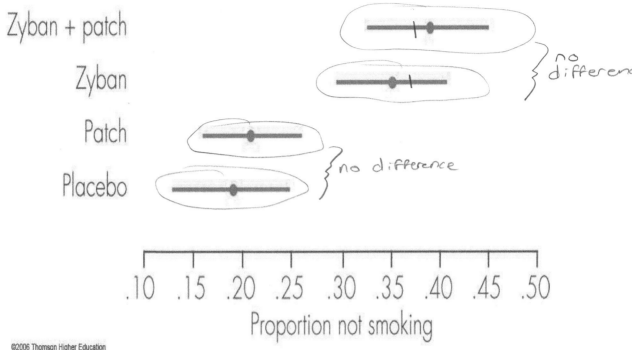

Zyban + patch

Zyban

Patch

Placebo

} no difference

} no difference

.10 .15 .20 .25 .30 .35 .40 .45 .50

Proportion not smoking

Overlapping CIs indicate no difference between the population proportions

(Zyban + patch) and (Zyban) alone are better than (placebo) and (patch)

Recommendation: Zyban alone

•**Example:** Is the proportion of males who smoke greater than the proportion of females who smoke? No, because CIs overlap

	Smokers	n
Males	30	120
Females	10	70

Construct a 99% C.I. for p, the true proportion of smokers for each group.

Males $(.148, .382)$ $\hat{p} = .25$

$(15\% - 35\%)$

Females $(.035, .251)$ $\hat{p} = .14$

$(3.5\% - 25\%)$

Problem: intervals are very wide!

Due to ① High C-level
② Sample sizes are too small

How large of a sample should I use? 99% C-level but I want to ↓ MOE to ±3%

$n = \hat{p}(1-\hat{p})\left(\frac{z^*}{E}\right)^2$ I need a value for $\hat{p}$

I can use $\hat{p} = 0.5$ (mid road)

or Total # smokers / total in both samples $= \frac{(30+10)}{(120+70)}$

$.21(1-.21)\left(\frac{2.576}{.03}\right)^2$

$\hat{p} = .21$

$n = 1224$ in each sample

306

How the Poll was conducted:

.95 or 95%

- In theory, in 19 cases out of 20, overall results based on such samples will differ by no more ~~tan~~ than 3 percentage points from what would have been obtained by seeking to interview all American adults.

Study: estimate p using $\hat{p} \pm MOE$

$$\hat{p} \pm 3\% \quad \downarrow \quad .03$$

95% CI estimate of p

0.6561

765   19.36

20.125   33.875

.0029798

+

92460   1100

60.3 - 63.7

72.5 - 75.3

42.076 ; 45.324   45.666 - 41.734

42.581 , 44.819

Chapter 11 - Part 1
Estimating a Mean with
a Confidence Interval

μ

Stat → test → #7-8 confidence intervals

We did A: 1Prop2Int

7: ZInterval: CI for μ → theoretical

① underlying population must be ≈ Normal

→ ② σ (the population st dev) must be
given → probably came from a
previous study

⁕ 8: TInterval: CI for μ → applied

① underlying population must be ≈ normal
if $n < 30$. If $n \geq 30$, we can relax that
required

② use s, the sample st dev as an estimate
of σ, the population st dev

Confidence Interval for a Population Mean

Population
What is value of parameter?

Ch 10 → estimate a population proportion → yes/no question

Ch 11 → population mean → measurement data

↓

Random sample
Use sample to estimate parameter

©2006 Thomson Higher Education

Ch 10 - use $\hat{p} \pm MOE$ to estimate p, pop proportion
  ↓ sample proportion

Ch 11 - use $\bar{x} \pm MOE$ to estimate μ, pop. mean
  ↓ sample mean

Confidence Interval for a Population Mean

- To create a confidence interval for a population mean:

  μ

  ### point estimate ± margin of error

- The margin of error is a 'table value' multiplied by 'the standard deviation of the sampling distribution of the sample mean'

$\bar{x} \pm$ table value $\cdot$ St dev

z table

7: Z interval $\bar{x} \pm (z) \cdot \sigma_{\bar{x}}$

8: t interval $\bar{x} \pm (t) \cdot s_{\bar{x}}$

t table

Confidence Interval for
a Population Mean μ
σ Known

pop. st dev

- The standard deviation of the sampling distribution of the sample mean is:

$$\frac{\sigma}{\sqrt{n}}$$

How do $\bar{x}_s$ behave?
in theory

$\bar{x} \sim N(\mu, \sigma/\sqrt{n})$

if underlying
pop is N

315

Confidence Interval for a Population Mean

- A confidence interval for μ in the special situation where:

  → The underlying population is approximately normal

  → The population standard deviation, σ, is a known value

  → Use a z-multiplier:

$$\underset{\text{Zinterval}}{} \quad \underset{\text{sample mean}}{\bar{x}} \pm z^* \cdot \underset{\substack{\text{sample} \\ \text{size}}}{\sigma / \sqrt{n}} \quad \underset{\substack{\text{pop st dev} \\ \text{from previous study}}}{}$$

Table ↗   theoretical method

Estimate avg starting salary of nurses in CT using 95% CI

$n = 100$

$\bar{x} = \$57000$

$$57000 \pm 1.96 \cdot \frac{\sigma}{\sqrt{100}} \qquad \sigma \rightarrow \text{I need this value}$$

Suppose I know from previous study $\sigma = 3000$

$(56,912, \ 58,088)$

$$5700 \pm \frac{58088 - 56912}{2}$$

$$\downarrow \pm 588$$

316

Confidence Interval for a Population Mean σ Unknown

- In most cases, the population standard deviation, σ, is an unknown value which is estimated from the sample data

- The standard error of the sample mean is the **estimated** standard deviation of the sampling distribution of the sample mean

$$s.e.(\overline{x}) = \frac{s}{\sqrt{n}}$$

s is a random variable; fluctuates from sample to sample

This fluctuation introduces another source of variation. We consequently move to a t-table instead of a z-table

Confidence Interval for a Population Mean

- The 'multiplier' is then a t-value from the **Student's t-distribution**

  → t-table

- The family of t-distributions:
  - Normal curves
  - Centered at 0
  - More spread out than the standard normal distribution
  - A parameter, called **degree of freedom (df)** is associated with each t-distribution
  - As **df** gets larger, the t-distribution gets close to the standard normal distribution

n − 1

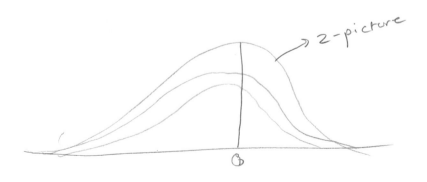

→ z-picture

Confidence Interval for a Population Mean

- For a confidence interval of a population mean, the t multiplier is the value, t* in a t-distribution with df = (n-1) such that the area between –t* and t* equals the desired confidence level.

Suppose n = 25
   df = 25 - 1 = 24
Suppose I want a
95% CI for μ

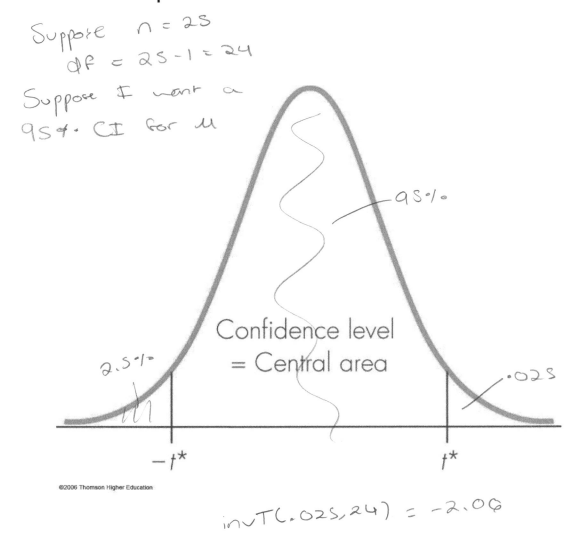

95%

Confidence level
= Central area

2.5%

.025

–t*   t*

@2006 Thomson Higher Education

invT(.025, 24) = -2.06

319

A Confidence Interval for A Population Mean

- A confidence interval for a population mean, μ, (also called a t-interval):

$$\bar{X} \pm t^* \cdot \frac{s}{\sqrt{n}}$$

table value

sample sd

Sample mean

Sample size

Compare this to z-interval

$$\bar{X} \pm z^* \cdot \frac{\sigma}{\sqrt{n}}$$

pop st dev; has to be known

Sample mean

z-table value

sample size

Confidence Interval for a Population Mean

- Situations for which a t-confidence interval for μ is valid:

    - Situation 1: The population of the measurements is normal and a random sample of any size is measured.

    - Situation 2: The population of measurements may not be normal, but a **large** random sample is observed. A somewhat arbitrary guideline of a "large" sample size is n ≥ 30, but if there are extreme outliers, a larger sample size may be required.

Confidence Interval for a Population Mean

μ use t-interval

- Before calculating a t-confidence interval for μ:

  – Plot the data in order to look for outliers and for skewness

  – If the sample size is small, decide whether the assumption of normality is nearly valid for the underlying population

If we use a t-interval

① underlying population must be ≈ normal for
    n < 30

② If n ≥ 30. we can say automatically ≈5%
    N based on CLT

Ex: A random sample of ~~n = 12~~ *—small sample*

we need to be concerned w/ possible lack of normality

University students were asked how much they spent on textbooks in a semester

- Data:

200	175	450	300	350	250
150	200	320	370	400	250

Boxplot to check for outliers
1st clear all y-registers

Normal prob. plot

nothing unusual

If this forms a fairly straight line, then data is ≈ normal

All good for using a t-interval
to estimate μ ↓ pop mean

use 95% CI

$(223.83, 345.34)$

$\bar{x} = 284.58$ $sx = 95.62$

$n = 12$

Confidence Interval for a Population Mean

Assume normality

- **Example 11.32**: Randomized study of the effectiveness of zinc lozenges in reducing the duration of cold symptoms.

- Zinc Group: n = 25, mean = 4.5 days, st. dev. = 1.6 days. (3.8, 5.2)

- Control Group: n = 23, mean = 8.1 days, st. dev. = 1.8 days

    (7.3, 8.9)

Zinc works!
(CIs don't overlap)

Confidence Interval for a Population Mean

- Interpreting a Confidence Interval for μ

    - Our confidence is in the procedure

      [handwritten: Not in the individual interval]

      [handwritten margin: unknown value we're trying to est.]

    - If we compute a 95% confidence interval for μ, we know that in the long run 95% of such intervals will actually contain μ

      [handwritten: incorrect]

    - We have no way of knowing whether the one interval that we have created actually does contain μ

Chapter 12 - Part 1
Testing a Hypothesis About a Proportion

Stat → tests
   Hyp test

1 Z test

※ 2 t test

3

4

※ 5 1Prop2Test

6

CI   theoretical

7 Z interval   estimate μ,

※ 8 t interval   population mean

9   applied

0

※ A 1Prop2Int → estimates p, pop proportion

B

Introduction to Hypothesis Tests:Coin Tossing

Coin: Is it fair or biased?

Collect data: Flipping the coin a large # of times
   record # of heads
           # of tails

$\widehat{X:}$ # of heads

Suppose I flip the coin 50 times

0 Biased ??? ——————— 25 ———————— ??? —— 50
                    Fair coin   Biased

What if I get 20H, 30T?
              15H, 35T?

To decide if the coin is fair or biased,
I need probability

What is P(20H, 30T) or more extreme
       if the coin is fair?

Introduction to Hypothesis Tests

- **Statistical hypothesis testing** uses data from a sample to judge whether or not a statement about a population parameter may be valid.

Problem: samples vary!

Ch 12 → use sample proportion $\hat{p}$ to make a decision about a population proportion, p

Formulating Hypotheses

•An inquiry may be expressed as a choice between two competing hypothesized statements:

$p > 50\%$

Example 12.1: Does a majority of the population favor a new legal standard for the minimum blood alcohol level that constitutes drunk driving?

opposites

Hypothesis 1: $p \leq .50$

Hypothesis 2: $p > .50$

researcher's hypothesis

Terminology for the Two Choices

• The **null hypothesis, H$_0$**:

Hypothesis of no change

Status quo hypothesis

• The **alternative hypothesis, H$_a$**:

researcher's hypothesis

Technique: proof by contradiction

Start by assuming H$_0$ is true

The researcher hopes that the sample data negates H$_0$ → negating H$_0$ means the data supports H$_a$

•**Example 1:** Suppose a pharmaceutical company wants to be able to claim that for its newest medication the <u>proportion of patients</u> who experience side effects is less tha<u>n 20%.</u>

H_0: $p = .20$

H_a: $p < .20$
⤷ one - tailed test

•**Example 2:** Suppose that a legislator plans to vote for a proposed blood alcohol limit if there is conclusive evidence that a majority of her constituents favor the proposal.

H_0: $p \leq .50$

H_a: $p > .50$
⤷ one-tailed test

•**Example 3:** Suppose a researcher wants to know if the proportion of left-handed students in his large elementary statistics class differs from the national proportion of left handed people. The national proportion is 10%.

H_0: $p = .10$

H_a: $p \neq .10$
↘ two-tailed test

•One-tailed hypothesis test:

$H_0 : p \geq .20$

$H_a : p < .20$

Assume $p = .20$

What values of $\hat{p}$ would support H_a?

possible $\hat{p}$ values would look like if $p = .20$

← .20

Values of $\hat{p}$ that would support H_a are values that would fall in the lower tail

•Two-tailed hypothesis test:

$H_0 : p = .10$

$H_a : p \neq .10$

Assume H_0 is true

possible $\hat{p}$ values assuming H_0 is true

.10

What value would support H_a?
Data that falls in either tail

The Logic of Hypothesis Testing

• In hypothesis testing, we assume that the null hypothesis is a possible truth until the sample data conclusively demonstrate otherwise.

— H_0

proof by contradiction

• We can only assess whether or not the observed data are consistent with an assumption that the null hypothesis is valid.

Start by assuming H_0 is true

Collect our sample data

• If the null hypothesis is valid about the population, what is the probability of observing sample data like that observed?

If the data is likely based on the assumption that H_0 is true, then we fail to reject H_0.

If the data is unlikely based on H_0 being true, then we reject H_0 in favor of H_a.

337

•**Example:** According to a study by Ipsos-Reid, 61% of Internet users aged 18-24 had downloaded music by the end of 2000. A researcher believes that the percentage is now higher than 61%. In a random sample of 1300 Internet users aged 18-24, he finds that 910 have downloaded music from the Internet.

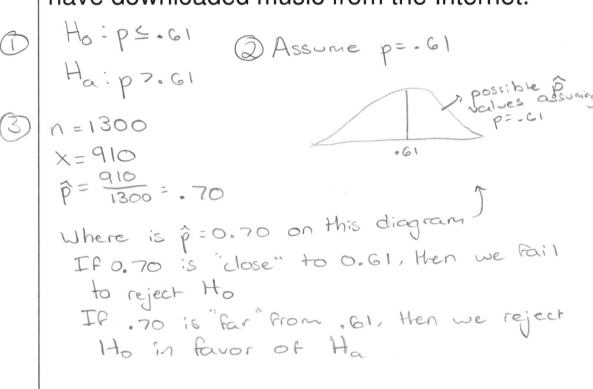

① $H_0: p \le .61$
$H_a: p > .61$

② Assume $p = .61$

③ $n = 1300$
$x = 910$
$\hat{p} = \frac{910}{1300} = .70$

possible $\hat{p}$ values assuming $p = .61$

Where is $\hat{p} = 0.70$ on this diagram?
If 0.70 is "close" to 0.61, then we fail to reject H_0
If $.70$ is "far" from $.61$, then we reject H_0 in favor of H_a

Reaching a Conclusion About the Two Hypotheses

- ## The **Test Statistic**

  Z-statistic — determine where $\hat{p}$ falls on the curve

  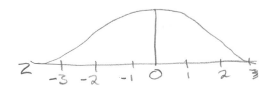

- ## The **p-value**

  goes w/ the z-statistic

  area in the tail associated
  w/ the z-statistic

  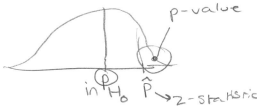

- ## The **level of significance**

  Alpha : α

  I pick this cutoff point

  This tells me how unlikely my results must be
  in order to reject H_0 in favor of H_a

Computing the Test Statistic for a Hypothesis Test about a Proportion

z-statistic

• A **Test Statistic** is a summary that compares the sample data to the null hypothesis. It is a standardized score based on the null hypothesis.

$$\text{Test Statistic} = \frac{\text{sample statistic} - \text{null value}}{\text{null standard error}}$$

$\hat{p}$ p_0

The probability of getting $\hat{p}$ of .70 or more if H_0 is true is almost impossible

Therefore we reject H_0 in favor of H_a

Computing the p-Value of a Hypothesis Test

•The **p-value** is computed by assuming that the null hypothesis is true and then determining the probability of a result as extreme (or more extreme) as the observed test statistic in the direction of the alternative hypothesis.

① $H_0 : p \leq .61$

$H_a : p > .61$

Data

   $x = 910$

   $n = 1300$

   $\hat{p} = .70$

($\Big($convert to a Z-statistic and a corresponding p-value

Stat → test → 5 : 1 Prop Z Test

   $P_0 = .61$

   $x : 910$ $n = 1300$

   prop $\neq P_0$ $<P_0$ $\boxed{>P_0}$ enter

   $Z = 6.65$

   $p \approx 0$

② Assume $p = .61$

6.65

$p \approx 0$

$\alpha = .05$

fail to reject H_0 .61

reject H_0 in favor of H_a

Choose an α-level for my hypothesis test

Typically these are α-levels that are used

   .01   .05   .10

Suppose I choose $\alpha = .05$

Rejecting the Null Hypothesis

We say results are

•Statistically significant: *if the data is far enough from the center of the curve that was drawn under the assumption that H_o is true*

How far is far enough?

•Level of significance or α level

We set this

A cutoff point in probability for deciding which hypothesis we believe the data supports

Typically we use one of these α-levels

.001   .005   .01   .025   .05   or .10

← harder to reject H_o

easier →

•In any statistical hypothesis test, the smaller the p-value is, the stronger is the evidence against the null hypothesis.

If p-value $< \alpha \Rightarrow$ we reject H_o in favor of H_a

If p-value $> \alpha \rightarrow$ we fail to reject H_o

Stating the Two Possible Conclusions

• When the p-value is small, we reject the null hypothesis.

• When the p-value is not small, we fail to reject the null hypothesis.

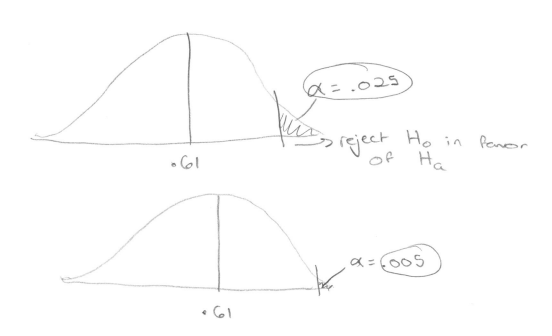

Example 12.6: If you are on a jury in the U.S. judicial system, you must presume that the defendant is innocent unless there is enough evidence to conclude that he or she is guilty.

H_0 : innocent

H_a : guilty

Start by assuming H_0 is true

Up to the state to present evidence that will convince the jury that the person is guilty

↑

proof by contradiction

Two Types of Errors

Let us use the courtroom analogy as an illustration. In the hypothesis testing framework, the two hypotheses are

- H_0: innocent
- H_a: guilty

The possible decisions are

- Fail to reject H_0: not enough evidence to "prove" guilt

- Reject H_0: evidence negates innocence, thus proving guilt

The possible errors are

Type 1 error ① Reject H_0 in favor of H_a, when in fact H_0 is true

      ↳ convict an innocent person

Type 2 error ② Fail to reject H_0, when in fact H_a is true

      ↳ acquit a guilty person

As the chances of Type 1 ↓, chances of Type 2 ↑

         Type 2 ↓

      Type 1 ↑

Type 1 and Type 2 Errors in Statistical Hypothesis Testing

•A **Type 1 error** can occur only when the null hypothesis is actually true. The error occurs by concluding that the alternative hypothesis is true.

H_0: new drug is not effective

H_a: new drug is effective

A Type 1 error → reject H_0 in favor of H_a when in fact H_0 is true

Result: individuals start using a new drug that actually isn't effective

•A **Type 2 error** can occur only when the alternative hypothesis is actually true. The error occurs by concluding that the null hypothesis cannot be rejected.

H_0: not effective

H_a: effective

A type 2 error → fail to reject H_0 when in fact H_a is true

Result: say drug isn't effective when it actually is

called "missed opportunity error"

346

Type 1 and Type 2 errors can be seen
this way:

	Defendant Innocent	Defendant guilty
Defendant Found Guilty	Type 1 error	Correct decision
Defendant Found Innocent	Correct decision	Type 2 error

	Ho True	Ho False
Reject Ho	Type 1 error	Correct decision
Fail to Reject Ho	Correct decision	Type 2 error

Probability of a Type 1 Error and the Level of Significance

Focus on Type 1 error → rejecting H_0 when in fact H_0 is true

We control this error w/ our hypothesis test set up

Type 1 error = level of significance = alpha level = α

Goal! I always want a small α-level

Typical α-levels

.001 .005 .01 .025 .05 .10

← I decrease the chances of a Type 1 error because I make it harder to reject H_0

(unfortunately I simultaneously increase a Type 2 error

Conditions for Conducting the z-Test

1.

2.

Example 12.12: Suppose that a pharmaceutical company wants to claim that side effects will be experienced by fewer than 20% of the patients who use a particular medication. In a clinical trial with 400 patients, they find that 68 patients experienced side effects.

1. Determine the null and alternative hypotheses.

$H_o: p \geq .20$

$H_a: p < \underline{.20}$

Data:

$n = 400$

$x = 68$

$\hat{p} = \dfrac{68}{400} = \underline{0.17}$

↳ random variable

we need to show $\hat{p}$ is far below .20

2. Verify necessary data conditions, and if they are met, summarize the data into an appropriate test statistic.

① Use random data

② "n" must be large enough

3. Assuming that the null hypothesis is true, find the p-value.

$H_0: p \geq .20$

$H_a: p < .20$

$x = 68$

$n = 400$

$\hat{p} = 0.17$

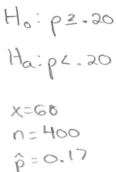

.067

.17 .20

Output: prop < .20

$z = -1.5$

p-value = .067

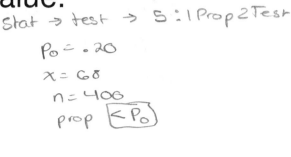

Stat → test → 5:1 Prop Z Test

$P_0 = .20$

$x = 68$

$n = 400$

prop $\boxed{< P_0}$

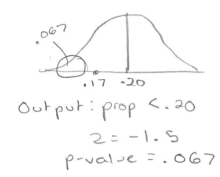

-1.5

4. Decide whether or not the result is statistically significant based on the p-value.

Now we need to look at α-levels

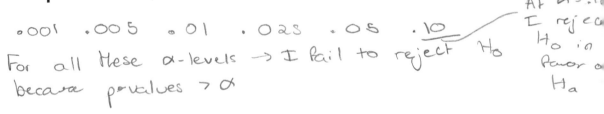

.001   .005   .01   .025   .05   .10

For all these α-levels → I fail to reject H_0

because p-values > α

At $\alpha = .10$

I reject H_0 in favor of H_a

5. Report the conclusion in the context of the problem.

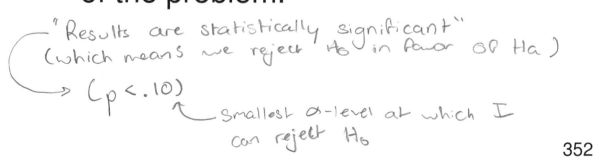

"Results are statistically significant"

(which means we reject H_0 in favor of H_a)

→ (p < .10)

↑ smallest α-level at which I can reject H_0

352

Chapter 13 - Part 1
Testing a Hypothesis About a Mean

Stat → test

1: Z test — theoretical

\#2: T test ⟩ about μ, population mean

\ applied

Testing a Hypothesis About a Population Mean: Subaru mpg

Subaru: Outbacks get on avg 27 mpg on highway

Consumer group: test this claim

$H_0: \mu \geq 27$

$H_a: \mu < 27$

Take a sample of a certain "n" of Outbacks

Calculate $\bar{x}$ and S

Assume $\mu = 27$

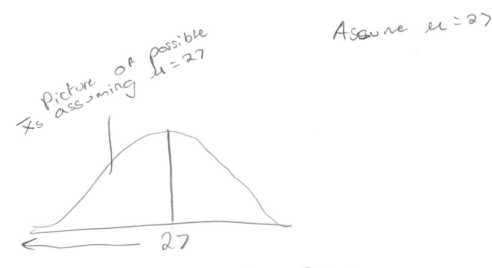

$\bar{x}$s Picture of possible assuming $\mu = 27$

27

How far is my $\bar{x}$ from 27 in lower tail

Testing a Hypothesis About a Population Mean

- Step 1: Determine the null and alternative hypotheses.

    - The Null Hypothesis:
        $H_0: \mu = \mu_0$

    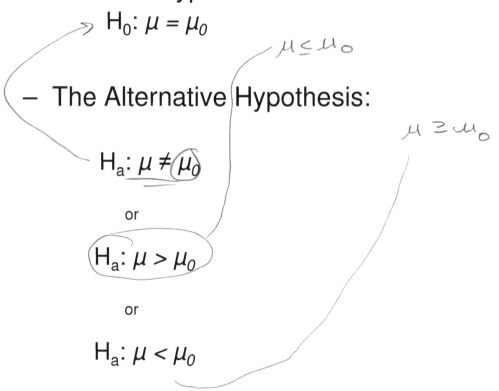

    - The Alternative Hypothesis:

        $H_a: \mu \neq \mu_0$

        or

        $H_a: \mu > \mu_0$

        or

        $H_a: \mu < \mu_0$

$\mu \leq \mu_0$

$\mu \geq \mu_0$

359

Testing Hypotheses About a Population Mean

- Step 2: Verify the necessary conditions and calculate the appropriate *test statistic*

- Situations for which a t-test for μ is valid:
  - Situation 1: The population of the measurements is normal and a random sample of any size is observed. In practice, the method is used as long as there is no evidence that the shape is notably skewed or that there are extreme outliers.

  - Situation 2: The population of measurements is not normal, but a **large** random sample is observed. A somewhat arbitrary definition of a "large" sample size is $n \geq 30$, but if there are extreme outliers, a larger sample may be required.

Testing a Hypothesis About a Population Mean:
σ Known

rarely the case (handwritten)

z-test (handwritten)

- The **test statistic** in the special situation where:
  - The underlying population is approximately normal
  - The population standard deviation, σ, is a known value

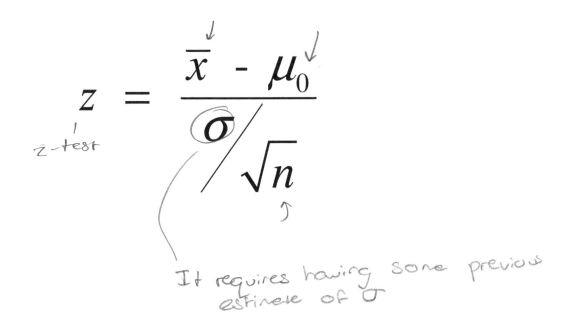

$$z = \frac{\bar{x} - \mu_0}{\sigma / \sqrt{n}}$$

z-test (handwritten)

It requires having some previous estimate of σ (handwritten)

Testing a Hypothesis About a Population Mean: σ Unknown

- In most cases, the population standard deviation, σ, is an unknown value which is estimated from the sample data

- The standard error of the sample mean is the **estimated** standard deviation of the sampling distribution of the sample mean

$$s.e.(\overline{x}) = \frac{s}{\sqrt{n}}$$

estimates $\frac{\sigma}{\sqrt{n}}$

Testing Hypotheses About a Population Mean: σ Unknown

- Step 3: The **test statistic** is then a
  t-statistic

$$t = \frac{\bar{x} - \mu_0}{s / \sqrt{n}}$$

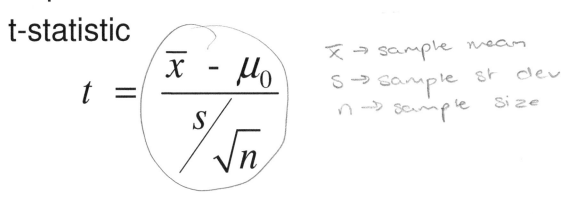

$\bar{x} \to$ sample mean
$s \to$ sample st dev
$n \to$ sample size

$\mu_0 \to$ hyp mean H_0

Testing Hypotheses about One Population Mean: σ Unknown

- Step 4: Decide whether or not the result is **statistically significant (H$_0$ is rejected)** based on the p-value

  - – Choose a significance level (α)
  - – The result is significant if the p-value ≤ α

  ↳ Typically:

  .001 .005 .01 .025 .05 .10

- Step 5: Report the conclusion within the context of the problem

  Comparing p-value to α

Example 13.1: Is normal body temperature actually lower than 98.6° F?

- Data was collected from a random sample of n = 16 individuals:

  98.4 98.6 98.8 98.8 98.0 97.9 98.5 97.6 98.4
  98.3 98.9 98.1 97.3 97.8 98.4 97.4

- Check for outliers/ extreme lack of normality with a Boxplot

Boxplot

normal prob plot → looking for a relatively straight line   No outliers

Fairly straign
so
Normality is
ok

Typical α-levels

.001 | .005 .01 .025 .05 .10

fail to reject H_0 .003   reject H_0 in favor of H_a

- Conduct a hypothesis test to determine whether normal body temperature is actually lower than 98.6° F

$H_0: \mu \geq 98.6$

$H_a: \mu < 98.6$

Stat → test

2: t-test

Data

List: L1
Freq: 1

$\mu \neq \mu_0$ $< \mu_0$ $> \mu_0$

Assume H_0 is true; represents possible $\bar{x}$s

98.6

Output
$\mu < 98.6$
$t = -3.22$
p-value = 0.003
$\bar{x} = 98.2$
s
n

Results are statistically significant $(p < .005)$

366

Ex: Testing tire pressure

- Many cars have a recommended tire pressure of 32 psi. Safety officials want to know whether cars on average have too little pressure in their tires. At a safety checkpoint, 50 cars are randomly selected and the tire pressure in the front left tire is measured. The average tire pressure for the 50 cars is 30.1 psi and the standard deviation is 3 psi. Carry out the appropriate hypothesis test.

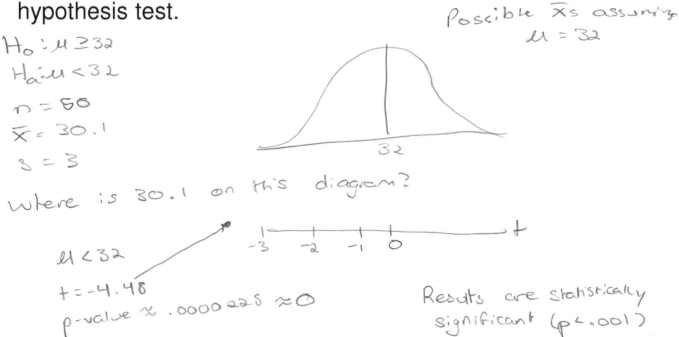

$H_o : \mu \geq 32$

$H_a : \mu < 32$

$n = 50$

$\bar{X} = 30.1$

$s = 3$

Where is 30.1 on this diagram?

Possible $\bar{X}$s assuming $\mu = 32$

32

$\mu < 32$

$t = -4.48$

p-value $\approx .0000225 \approx 0$

-3   -2   -1   0

Results are statistically significant ($p < .001$)

Chapter 10 - Part 2
Confidence Interval for the Difference
in Two Population Proportions

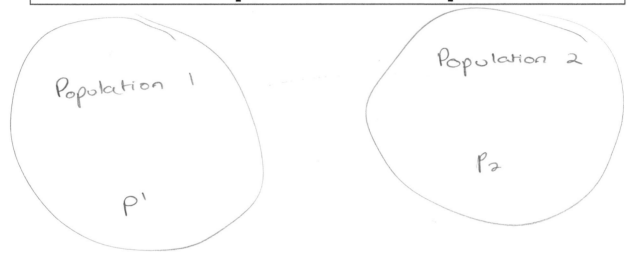

Population 1

P_1

Population 2

P_2

point estimate ± margin of error

Table value

A confidence interval for p₁-p₂ is:

$$\left(\hat{p}_1 - \hat{p}_2\right) \pm z^* \sqrt{\frac{\hat{p}_1\left(1-\hat{p}_1\right)}{n_1} + \frac{\hat{p}_2\left(1-\hat{p}_2\right)}{n_2}}$$

s.e. of $(\hat{p}_1 - \hat{p}_2)$ s

•**Example 10.10:** Is there a difference between the proportion of 12th grade females who always wear a seatbelt when driving and the proportion of 12th grade males who always wear a seatbelt when driving?

Sex	X = # of yes	n
1 Female	915	1467
2 Male	771	1575

Form a 95% confidence interval for the difference between these two proportions.

Stat → test → B:2 Prop2Int → 915/1467

(0.099, 0.169) $\hat{p}_1 = .624$

   +   + $\hat{p}_2 = .490$ 771/1575

The proportion of all females who always wear seatbelts is between __10%__ and __17%__ higher than the proportion of males

Interpreting the Outcomes of a Two Proportion Confidence Interval

$(+, +)$ population proportion for Group 1 is higher than the population proportion for Group 2

$(-, -)$ Group 1 population proportion is lower than Group 2 pop prop

$(-, +)$ Since this interval contains 0, we have to assume there is no difference in pop props

Example: Is the proportion of males who smoke greater than the proportion of females who smoke?

	Smokers	n
1) Males	30	120
2) Females	10	70

Construct a 99% C.I. for the difference between the proportion of smokers in each group.

B: 2 Prop Z Int

$(-0.041, 0.255) \rightarrow$ no difference

$\hat{p}_1 = .25$

$\hat{p}_2 = .14$

2 problems that cause such a wide CI
   ① Sample sizes are small → solution = more data
   ② CL is high: 99% → lower this to 95%

Chapter 11 - Part 2
Estimating Means with Confidence: Independent and Dependent Samples

Paired Data (Dependent Samples)
vs.
Independent Samples

- Paired data: Parameter of interest is μ_d

  - What is the mean improvement in reading scores for all 5th graders in Hartford before and after an enhancement program?

- Independent samples: Parameter of interest is $\mu_1 - \mu_2$

  - What is the difference in the mean survival times of independent samples of cancer patients receiving radiation vs. cancer patients receiving chemotherapy?

Paired Data

- Paired data: Data has been observed in natural pairs

  or each person

  - Each unit has two measurements
    - Example: Pretest and posttest scores

  - Similar individuals are paired
    - Example: An experiment involving 2 treatments and each twin receives a different treatment

1. L1 ○   L2 ○ → individuals are paired in some way

CI for the Population Mean of Paired Differences

- Data:

  Two Observations from each of *n* pairs

  Calculate a difference for each pair of observations: $d = x_1 - x_2$

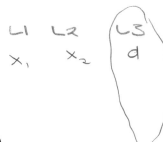

- Population parameter: μ_d = mean of the population of differences

  Trying to estimate avg difference

  same as $\bar{x}$

  Sample estimate of μ_d:

  $\bar{d}$ = sample mean of the n differences

  Standard error :

  $$s.e.(\overline{d}) = \frac{s_d}{\sqrt{n}}$$

CI for the Population Mean of Paired Differences

- Confidence Interval for μ_d:

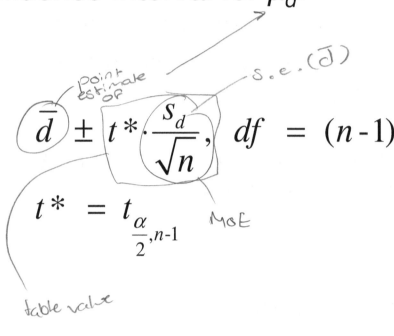

$$\overline{d} \pm t^* \cdot \frac{s_d}{\sqrt{n}}, \quad df = (n-1)$$

$$t^* = t_{\frac{\alpha}{2}, n-1}$$

point estimate of

s.e. $(\overline{d})$

MOE

table value

$$\overline{x} \pm t \cdot \frac{s}{\sqrt{n}}$$

t - interval

CI for the Population Mean of Paired Differences

- Situations for which a t-confidence interval for μ_d is valid:

  - Situation 1: The population of differences is normal and a random sample of any size is measured

  - Situation 2: The population of differences may not be normal, but a **large** random sample is observed. A somewhat arbitrary guideline of a "large" sample size is $n \geq 30$, but if there are extreme outliers, a larger sample size may be required.

Example: Lowering Blood Pressure

- Can individuals with high blood pressure lower their blood pressure through meditation?   A study was ~~small sample~~ conducted with 15 volunteers who agreed to learn meditation techniques to attempt to lower blood pressure. Use the sample data to construct a 95% CI for μ_d. Make sure to check that the conditions for the CI are satisfied before constructing the interval.

small sample

— normality
—no outliers

Example (cont.): Lowering Blood Pressure

Subject	x_1 BPBefore	x_2 BPAfter	$x_1 - x_2$ Difference
1	165	162	3
2	156	150	6
3	141	132	9
4	171	172	-1
5	140	138	2
6	138	130	8
7	155	148	7
8	180	170	10
9	152	140	12
10	166	161	5
11	145	145	0
12	143	137	6
13	137	121	16
14	139	136	3
15	152	141	11

If meditation works, then typically our differences should be positive

385

Example (cont.): Lowering Blood Pressure

CI for μ_d

If meditation works, we would expect a positive difference in the values

Stat → test → 8: T interval

$(3.9, 9.1)$ → Both values are positive

Avg drop in BP after meditating is b/t 4 and 9 points using 95% CI

Independent Samples

- Independent samples: measurements on one sample are <u>not related</u> to the measurements on the other sample

    - Independent random samples are taken separately from two populations
        - Example: Final grades in an on-line statistics course and final grades in a traditional statistics class taken by 2 independent samples of students

    - Participants are randomly assigned to one of two treatment groups
        - Example: Randomly assign individuals to take a new prescription drug and randomly assign other individuals to take a placebo

387

CI for the Difference in Two Population Means

less restrictive test/CI doesn't make assumption $\sigma_1 = \sigma_2$

- The General (Unpooled) Case

  Data: from two populations or groups with standard deviations σ_1 and σ_2 from which independent samples are available

  The notation is as follows:

	Population Mean	Sample Size	Sample Mean	Sample Standard Deviation
Population 1	μ_1	n_1	$\bar{x}_1$	s_1
Population 2	μ_2	n_2	$\bar{x}_2$	s_2

  ©2006 Thomson Higher Education

- Population parameter: $\mu_1 - \mu_2$ = difference in the two population means

CI for the Difference in Two Population Means

- $100(1-\alpha)$ Confidence Interval for $\mu_1 - \mu_2$:

  90 %.
  or
  95 %
  or
  98 %
  or
  99 %.

  2 Sample T interval to estimate $\mu_1 - \mu_2$

  Results
  $(+, +) \rightarrow \mu_1$ exceeds μ_2
  $(-, -) \rightarrow \mu_1$ is less than μ_2
  $(-, +) \rightarrow$ no difference

CI for the Difference in Two Population Means

- Situations for which a t-confidence interval for $\mu_1 - \mu_2$ is valid:

  - Situation 1: The populations of measurements are both normal and random samples of any size is measured

  - Situation 2: Large random samples are measured. A somewhat arbitrary definition of "large" sample size is $n_1 \geq 30$, $n_2 \geq 30$, but if there are extreme outliers, a larger sample may be required.

- Here is the resting pulse rate data:

Exercisers: 62 72 60 63 75 64 60 52 64 80 68 64

Non-exercisers: 72 84 66 72 62 84 76 60

estimate $\mu_1 - \mu_2$

Stat → rest → 0: 2 Sample T Interval

$(-15.06, 1.7274)$

$(-, +)$

no difference

looks as if exercising might lower pulserates on avg

go get more data

391

Example: Calculate a 95% confidence interval for the Difference in mean resting pulse rates for Individuals who exercise vs. individuals Who do not exercise.

Chapter 12 - Part 2
Testing Hypotheses About the Difference in Two Population Proportions

6:2Prop Z Test

The Null and Alternative Hypothesis

H_0: $p_1 - p_2 = 0$ No difference

$\quad\quad\quad p_1 = p_2$

H_a: $p_1 - p_2 \neq 0$ 2-tailed $\longrightarrow p_1 \neq p_2$

H_a: $p_1 - p_2 > 0$ 1-tailed $\longrightarrow p_1 > p_2$

H_a: $p_1 - p_2 < 0$ 1-tailed $\longrightarrow p_1 < p_2$

397

Example: On the basis of its biochemical properties, it was hypothesized that regular use of the sweetener xylitol might be useful for preventing ear infections in preschool children. In a randomized experiment, n_1 = 165 children took five daily doses of placebo syrup, and 68 of these children got an ear infection during the study. Another n_2 = 159 children took five daily doses of xylitol, and 46 of these children got an ear infection during the study.

placebo
$n_1 = 165$
$x_1 = 68$

xylitol
$n_2 = 159$
$x_2 = 46$

1. Determine the null and alternative hypotheses.

$H_0: p_1 = p_2$

$H_a: p_1 > p_2$ if xylitol works

2. Verify necessary data conditions, and if they are met, summarize the data into an appropriate test statistic.

① Random samples

② Samples must be large enough

Rule: $n \cdot \hat{p} \geq 10$ $165\left(\frac{68}{165}\right) \geq 10$

$n \cdot (1-\hat{p}) \geq 10$

3. Assuming that the null hypothesis is true, find the p-value.

$H_0: p_1 = p_2$

$H_a: p_1 > p_2$

Stat → test → 6: 2prop2test

$z = 2.31$

p-value = 0.0103

$\hat{p}_1 = .41$

$\hat{p}_2 = .29$

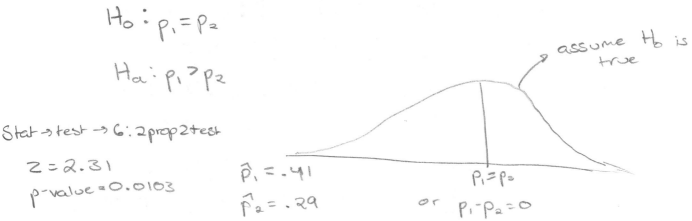

assume H_0 is true

$p_1 = p_2$

or $p_1 - p_2 = 0$

4. Decide whether or not the result is statistically significant based on the p-value.

→ I need possible α-levels: .0103

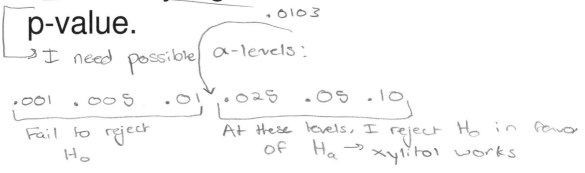

.001 .005 .01   .025 .05 .10

Fail to reject H_0

At these levels, I reject H_0 in favor of H_a → xylitol works

5. Make a conclusion in the context of the problem.

Research paper: results are statistically significant (p < .025)

Ex. 12.69: A Gallup poll asked the question: "Do you feel that the laws covering firearms should be made "more strict?" Of the 493 men, 52% said 'yes,' while of the 538 women, 72% said 'yes.' Is there sufficient evidence to conclude that a higher proportion of women in the population than men think these laws should be made more strict?

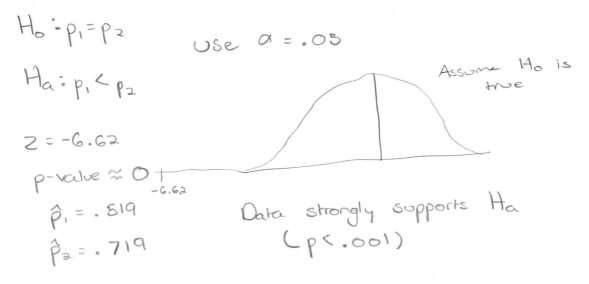

$H_o : p_1 = p_2$ Use $\alpha = .05$

$H_a : p_1 < p_2$ Assume H_o is true

$Z = -6.62$

p-value ≈ 0
          -6.62

$\hat{p}_1 = .519$

$\hat{p}_2 = .719$ Data strongly supports H_a
          $(p < .001)$

Chapter 13 - Part 2
Testing Hypotheses About Means: Independent And Dependent Samples

Testing Hypotheses About the Population Mean of Paired Differences

- Paired Data:

  - data that is collected in natural pairs

  - The researcher is interested in the **differences**, not the original observations

  - Often the researcher is interested in whether the mean difference in the population is **different from 0**. This is accomplished by a **paired t-test**

Testing Hypotheses About the Population Mean of Paired Differences

- Data:

  Two observations for each of n individuals, or pairs

  Calculate a difference for each pair of observations: $d = x_1 - x_2$

- Population parameter: μ_d = mean of the population of differences

  Sample estimate of μ_d :

  $\bar{d}$ = sample mean of the differences

  Standard error :

  $$s.e.(\bar{d}) = \frac{s_d}{\sqrt{n}}$$

Testing Hypotheses about the Population Mean of Paired Differences

- Determine the null and alternative hypotheses

  - The Null Hypothesis:

    $H_0: \mu_d = 0$ paired t-test

  - The Alternative Hypothesis:

    $H_a: \mu_d \neq 0$ 2-tailed

    or

    $H_a: \mu_d > 0$ 1-tailed

    or

    $H_a: \mu_d < 0$ 1-tailed

Testing Hypotheses about the Population Mean of Paired Differences

- Verify the required conditions and calculate the appropriate **test statistic**

- Situations for which a t-test for μ_d is valid:
  - Situation 1: The population of the differences is normal and a random sample of any size is measured. In practice, the method is used as long as there is no evidence that the shape is notably skewed or that there are extreme outliers.

  - Situation 2: The population of differences is not normal, but a **large** random sample is observed. A somewhat arbitrary definition of a "large" sample size is $n \geq 30$, but if there are extreme outliers, a larger sample may be required.

Testing Hypotheses about the Population Mean of Paired Differences

- The **test statistic** is then a t-statistic

$$t = \frac{\bar{d} - 0}{s_d / \sqrt{n}}$$

$\bar{x}$

$s / \sqrt{n}$

2: Ttest

Testing Hypotheses about the Population Mean of Paired Differences

- Find the p-value

- Decide whether or not the result is **statistically significant** based on the p-value

- Report the conclusion within the context of the problem

Example: Anxiety about visiting the dentist. Researchers want to know if this affects blood pressure.

- ## Data:
  - BP Before: BP After:

ind's

BP Before	BP After
1. 132	118
2. 135	137
149	140
133	139
119	107
121	116
128	122
132	124
119	115
10. 110	103

Paired data

I need a column of differences

Example: Anxiety about visiting the dentist. Researchers want to know if this affects blood pressure.

- Boxplots: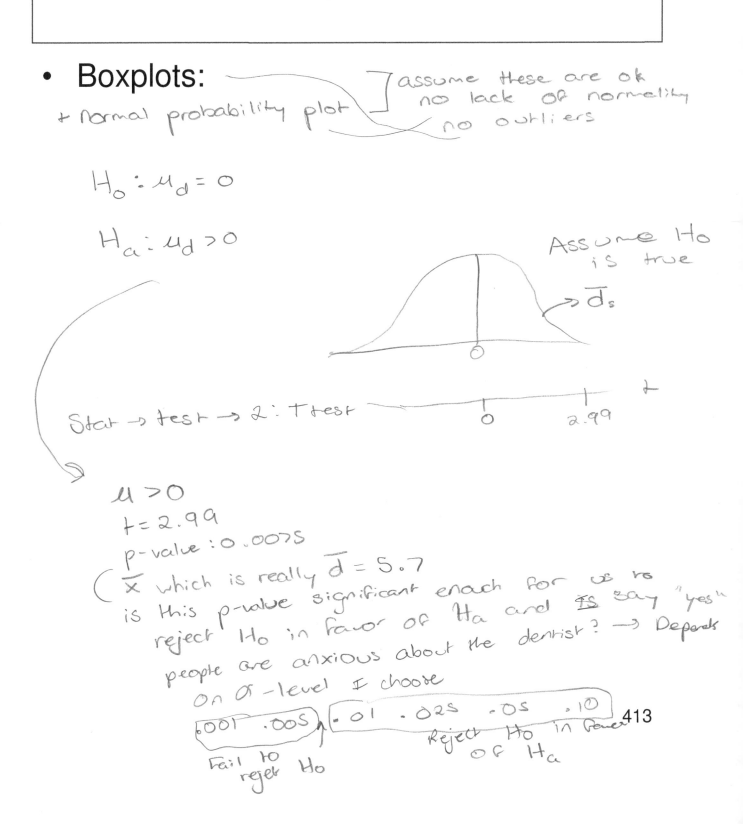

+ normal probability plot   ] assume these are ok
                                no lack of normality
                                no outliers

$H_o : \mu_d = 0$

$H_a : \mu_d > 0$

Assume Ho is true

$\rightarrow \bar{d}_s$

Stat → test → 2: T test

$\mu > 0$
$t = 2.99$
p-value : 0.0075
($\bar{x}$ which is really $\bar{d} = 5.7$
is this p-value significant enach for us to
reject Ho in favor of Ha and IS say "yes"
people are anxious about the dentist? → Depends

On σ−level I choose

.001   .005   .01   .025   .05   .10

Fail to reject Ho

Reject Ho in Favor of Ha

413

- Determine the null and alternative hypotheses

- The Null Hypothesis:

$$H_0: \mu_1 - \mu_2 = 0 \quad \rightarrow \mu_1 = \mu_2$$

  – The Alternative Hypothesis:

$$H_a: \mu_1 - \mu_2 \neq 0 \quad \mu_1 \neq \mu_2$$

  or

$$H_a: \mu_1 - \mu_2 > 0 \quad \mu_1 > \mu_2$$

  or

$$H_a: \mu_1 - \mu_2 < 0 \quad \mu_1 < \mu_2$$

Testing Hypotheses About the Difference in Two Population Means (Unpooled Case)

- Verify the necessary conditions and calculate the appropriate **test statistic**

- Situations for which a two sample t-test for the difference in two population means is valid:
  - Situation 1: Both populations of the measurements are approximately normal and are random samples of any size. In practice, the method is used as long as there is no evidence that the shapes are notably skewed or that there are extreme outliers.

  - Situation 2: The populations of measurements are not approximately normal, but *large* random samples are observed. A somewhat arbitrary definition of "large" sample sizes is $n_1 \geq 30$, $n_2 \geq 30$, but if there are extreme outliers, larger samples may be required.

  - In either situation, the samples must be independent

Testing Hypotheses About the Difference in Two Population Means (Unpooled Case)

- The **test statistic** is

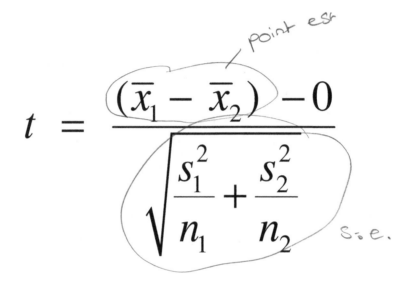

$$t = \frac{(\bar{x}_1 - \bar{x}_2) - 0}{\sqrt{\dfrac{s_1^2}{n_1} + \dfrac{s_2^2}{n_2}}}$$

point est

S.e.

Testing Hypotheses About the Difference in Two Population Means (Unpooled Case)

- Find the p-value

- Decide whether or not the result is **statistically significant** based on the p-value

  Typically we choose one of these α-levels

  .001 .005 .01 .025 .05 .10

- Report the conclusion within the context of the problem

Ex: Do Organized Study Groups Result in Higher Grades?

- In this study, Statistics 1100 students were randomly assigned to one of two groups.

  Group 1: Participated in a regular weekly study group throughout the semester

  Group 2: Control group

  Results at the end of the semester:

  Group 1: The group of 75 students had a mean score of 85 at the end of the semester with a standard deviation of 4.

  Group 2: The group of 70 students had a mean score of 78 at the end of the semester with a standard deviation of 7.5.

Ex: Do Organized Study Groups Result in Higher Grades?

- Conduct a two sample t-test.

Group 1

$n_1 = 75$

$\overline{x}_1 = 85$

$s_1 = 4$

Group 2

$n_2 = 70$

$\overline{x}_2 = 78$

$s_2 = 7.5$

$H_0: \mu_1 = \mu_2$

$H_a: \mu_1 > \mu_2$

$\mu_1 - \mu_2 = 0$

Stat → test → 4: 2 Sample T test

$\mu_1 > \mu_2$

$t = 6.94$

p-value ≈ 0

≈ 0

6.94

Results are Statistically significant (p < .001)